The Complete Chief Officer

by

Captain Michael Lloyd FNI

Witherby Seamanship International
A Division of Witherby Publishing Group Ltd
4 Dunlop Square, Livingston, Edinburgh, EH54 8SB, Scotland, UK
Tel No: +44(0)1506 463 227 - Fax No: +44(0)1506 468 999
Email: info@emailws.com - Web: www.witherbyseamanship.com

First edition published 2010

ISBN 978 1 85609 359 0

British Library Cataloguing in Publication Data
A catalogue record for this book is available from the British Library.

Printed and bound in Great Britain by Bell & Bain Ltd, Glasgow

Published by

Witherby Publishing Group Ltd
4 Dunlop Square, Livingston,
Edinburgh, EH54 8SB,
Scotland, UK

Tel No: +44(0)1506 463 227
Fax No: +44(0)1506 468 999

Email: info@emailws.com
Web: www.witherbys.com

Dedicated to
Captain Terrence Ford
1946-2009

'And now the old ships and their men are gone; the new ships and the new men, many of them bearing the old, auspicious names, have taken up their watch on the stern and impartial sea, which offers no opportunities but to those who know how to grasp them with a ready hand and an undaunted heart.'

Joseph Conrad 1857 - 1924

As Chief Officer you don't know what type of ship you will be tasked with running, and what challenges that will present on a day-to-day basis.

Contents

The Complete Chief Officer

Author's Introduction

When I first went to sea as a cadet, and later as a junior officer, I cannot remember being particularly interested in the ships I was on. I was proud of their general appearance in comparison to others, but the reason why tasks were done, the running of the ship and all the other facets of shipboard life were not in my sphere of responsibility. I did my job, generally just enough to keep everyone off my back, but I was more interested in the ports that we went to, the sights that we passed and of course the runs ashore. In other words, although I did my job and was happy doing it, I had not accepted that this was my career. It was an interesting and fun way to pass a few years before coming ashore and settling down into the 'real' job that relatives frequently alluded to.

I was a seaman though; I could hardly not have been with two years on *HMS Conway* and then a three year cadetship. However, on becoming an officer, the seamanship side declined and navigation and cargo work came to the fore, particularly as Second Officer, where I basically became an office worker who worked during the quiet hours.

One day, when the slot needed filling, I was promoted to Chief Officer, or 'Mate', and a new world was before me. The ship was mine and its appearance and the day-to-day efficiency would reflect my ability. I am not saying that the chrysalis opened and a butterfly emerged, but for the first time I became really interested in the ship. The fascinating world of seamanship once again opened to me, and from that moment on I became immersed in the sea and ships, enjoying both to the extent that I never left.

This book is for the young officer aspiring to the position of Chief Officer, or one who has recently been promoted into the position. It is a practical book dealing in the 'real world' of the sea and ships rather than the theoretical, and it discusses the various problems that can be encountered as the Mate of a ship. There are many publications that teach the correct way of performing the multitude of tasks making up our profession. These publications can be helpful and many of the specialist subjects dealt with are essential. But what we are trying to learn constantly at sea, whatever our rank or experience, is how to blend the 'correct' with the 'possible' to produce a feasible result that will get us and the ship through another day unscathed.

In my book, 'In Command', I briefly touched on the rank of Chief Officer, mostly dealing with the Captain's relationship. However, I did not relate the essential nature of this officer's contribution to the successful running of a ship. Looking back at my time in command, the most successful and happy times were when, together with the Chief Engineer and Chief Officer, we formed a team responsible for our own spheres of interest but assisting each other when required. When a ship has such a team at the top, it is the most professional and efficient method of ship management and a formidable faction to interfere with.

When you consider that, apart from the general upkeep of the ship, the Chief Officer is responsible for the loading, stowage and discharge of all the cargo, which is the whole purpose of the ship, it is surprising that many companies, although taking care with the appointments of the Master and Chief Engineer, are so lacking in concern with the Chief Officer. Few shipping companies are willing to recognise that the Chief Officer of a ship has more direct responsibility than any department manager ashore, or accord the rank the respect it deserves.

It is probably thought that, as the Captain is present and his background is the deck department, if the Chief Officer is lacking in ability the Captain will make up for it. This premise is of course unsound, as the Captain has enough to do on a busy ship and it could well be that he is unfamiliar with aspects of the ship's cargoes, the stability and the stowage calculations of the ship he is commanding. Neither is it the Captain's job. If he should do this then he is effectively taking away the expected responsibility of the Chief Officer. If we remove this then at what stage do we give it back? When he is the Captain? But if he is not used to having responsibility as a Chief Officer, how will he be the effective Captain that the industry constantly declares is essential for the safe and efficient progress of a ship on the seas?

Somehow, in many companies, we would seem to have lost our way in the ability to trust our officers, and even our Captains, to do what they are trained for. If they are not trusted with the tasks that their rank and certificate deem them capable of doing then their interest in the work as a whole declines and the efficiency of the ship suffers, to the detriment of the company.

If this decline in trust of the officers continues the industry is, by default, admitting that there is a failure in the training system as a whole.

If a company has trusted the ship to qualified officers then, by providing guidelines rather than regulation, it should allow the flexibility of the intelligence of those officers to benefit the ship and company. This will acknowledge and enhance the bond between ship and shore rather than fostering the resentment of office intrusion that many feel interferes with the management of the ship.

Of all the jobs onboard, the Mate's position can be the most satisfying and the most frustrating. You will know what needs to be done but you may not always have the men, resources and support to do it. You will want your ship smart and 'shipshape', but your company might not be willing to pay for this.

You will encounter some or all of these problems and, if you are a professional officer, manage to cope with them while doing your job to the best of your ability. How long you intend to remain at sea is not relevant; to have been a complete Chief Officer will guarantee your confidence in your capabilities at sea and in any other occupation you may find yourself. Above all, looking back, you will be proud of what you accomplished.

Captain Michael Lloyd
April 2010

1 The Chief Officer

The Chief Officer is basically a day-to-day man, directly concerned with what actually is and letting those higher up the food chain worry about the future. If recently promoted, you will have moved from junior officer to senior officer and, apart from a larger cabin, should have an office, or at least a desk, and a dramatic shift in responsibility. Theoretically, you are Chief Officer because those operating the ship deemed you worthy and knowledgeable enough for this position. In reality, it may be that there was no one else around! Regardless of the 'how', here you are and the successful operation of the ship is considerably dependent on you.

Given adequate manning, the proper equipment, good departmental officers and a supportive Captain, the Chief Officer's job can be the best job afloat. Unfortunately, very few will have the manning levels required to maintain and operate the ship properly and efficiently. Your equipment could be poorly cared for. Your department could be of poor ability and your Captain not as you would wish. But it is *your* job to surmount these obstacles and ensure that the ship is efficient in all aspects where you have jurisdiction.

Regardless of what you walk into, you are still the Mate of the ship and your success will depend not only on your abilities, but also your attitude. It is a position that requires you to lead from the front. For any problem not involving the engines, you are the person that others will come to and, in some mysterious way, you are expected to solve it. You are the fixer and you must do all you can to keep the job moving.

Inevitably throughout this book, your relationship with the Captain will frequently be referred to. In the past, I have heard Chief Officers say that they "*didn't care what the Captain thought as they worked for the company not for him*". Do not make this grave error. You work for the company through him and, if he were to decide, his seniority may mean that you might have to start looking for another job. Don't forget the other Captains in the company are his colleagues and quick e-mails can assure you of a hot reception on the other ships in the fleet.

You will feel the scrutiny of your presentation and actions.

The greatest asset to the position of Chief Officer, apart from confidence, is common sense. You are not required or expected to have every finger a marlin spike, or have an affinity with parrots or rum. If you do your best for the Captain and the ship, you will be the Chief Officer most companies and Captains want to have running their ships.

2 Your Company

If you have the luxury of your choice of company or ship type, think carefully about the experience you want to gain in the pursuit of your future career. If you intend hanging on a few years to get your Master's certificate or get a few more years experience and go ashore, by all means jump on a cruise ship and have a last few years of fun.

On the other hand, if you are interested in increasing your seamanship experience and professional abilities before choosing your seagoing career path or looking for promotion to Master on ability, you should look further afield. Don't be wary of trying something different as this is the time that you will really begin to immerse yourself in your profession. Of course, you cannot go immediately onto a sophisticated ship such as a gas carrier as Chief Officer without previous experience and the necessary cargo endorsements, but there is nothing wrong in signing on as a second officer for a few voyages. In other words, don't be too anxious to become Chief Officer if you would like to move around for a while. Strangely enough you can, without any previous experience, go onto what are recognised as the most dangerous ships afloat, ie bulk carriers. Be very careful!

Capesize bulker – No previous experience required - apply within.

Another question that will affect your choice of ship is what you want out of your career. If you want financial rewards and to enjoy yourself on leave rather than seeing the world, then tankers or gas carriers are for you. These are like floating factories, generally owned by well-regulated companies with good leave and pay conditions but rigidly controlled from ashore. On the other hand, if you want to live a lifestyle like that ashore, have fun and be paid for it, then cruise ships are for you. If you want seamanship, promotion on ability, the chance of adventure, or at least a more interesting way of life and to see the world, then the companies operating differing ships on worldwide trades or the specialist areas such as support ships, salvage and ship delivery might be your choice. Obviously there are many more types of ships to consider. All I am suggesting is that, these days, the company is not from birth to death. While in the past they could choose you, at the moment you can choose them. Make the most of this as it is unlikely to last.

We must now assume that you do have some familiarity with the job you are going to do. Promotion from within will have been the easier course as you and the company are known quantities, although this can work both ways.

Regardless of the company, they all operate from a head office, although whether you ever see this depends on your position where you are employed. If the head office is thousands of miles away you could be employed through a regional office, or you may live on the Indian sub-continent and be employed by an agency, in which case you will be flown directly to the ship.

It is to be hoped that the company will have looked at your CV and found the experience that they wanted, but do not depend on this.

I remember being sent out to do a deep sea tow with no experience whatsoever. When I pointed out to the company that they advertised the experience of their crews, their answer was, "what the charterers did not know would not hurt them" and that I would pick it up on the way. I arrived at the ship to meet a Captain quite rightly irate at my inexperience, and was faced with a brand new 9 inch tow wire still wrapped in burlap and with no eye splice, and the tow starting in 24 hours. We pulled the tucks through with a 5 ton winch, even putting in a Liverpool tuck, served and parcelled it and away we went. I am pleased to say that, after a few incidents when I was more a hindrance than a help, all went well and when we uncoupled the splice it was as good as new. In other words, I got away with it.

Courtesy MCA

What happens on your next trip could well be a surprise.

The moral of the tale is to be sensible. If the company or agency employing you is sending you out to do a job that you have never done or been trained for, and if that job could cause danger to life by your lack of knowledge, look elsewhere. I was stupid to have gone on a deep sea towing ship as Mate without experience and might well have felt the same anger as that Master if I had been in his position. However, if you are told that you are joining a container ship but find yourself on a heavy lift vessel, there is not much you can do except explain the position and hopefully lean heavily on the Master.

There are companies that tend to engage in social experimentation, almost as if their seafarers were animals in a laboratory. New equipment must always be accepted, new methods often go together with new ships, but too many seafarers suffer trying to implement social policies that do not work, causing problems, both professional and personal, on the ships.

Looking back over the years, I remember the disaster of joining all the crew and officers in one bar in a well known tanker company. Another company tried abandoning uniforms and the title of Captain, instead using 'ship manager', yet another failure. At the moment, a tanker company is trying 'dual command' and a large company is attempting to ban alcohol. Both of these experiments are causing problems with administration and morale.

Find out if your company is relatively conventional in leaving well alone and if your responsibilities are the traditionally accepted ones, ie that you are the responsible head of the deck department. If you discover, for example, that the Chief Engineer is in charge of all maintenance and you are responsible to him, you must decide whether or not you need the job badly enough.

Check your contract and make sure that your medical care and repatriation are taken care of and clarify the compassionate leave policy if there is one. Find out what currency your pay is in. In these days of fluctuating currency rates it is far better to have your pay in your own home currency at an agreed exchange rate, so that your pay remains steady throughout your employment.

You will have some tell-tale signs about the quality of the company before you reach the gangway.

It might seem a small point, but find out the standard of hotels the company puts their senior officers in. There is a good chance that you will have some time in a hotel when either joining or leaving the vessel, and you don't want to find yourself in a dockside doss house. It is also a very good indicator of how they regard you. If you know the company's policy, when the agent on arrival takes you to a mud hut by the railway track instead of the Holiday Inn, pocketing the difference, you can threaten to contact the company. This is a widespread racket, with shipping companies often being blamed for treating their crews badly when it is a corrupt practice worked by the agencies. Occasionally even the agency doesn't know what their employees are up to.

I was once sent to join a ship and taken to a grubby little hotel and told that this was the standard one. The shipping company concerned was a decent one that would never have ordered this so I installed myself in a better hotel and next morning joined the ship. On advising the Captain of what had happened, and after hearing the complaints from other officers who had suffered the same experience, he advised the company of the situation. They found that they were being billed for far superior hotels and immediately started proceedings that uncovered a large-scale racket being worked by the employees of quite a large agency.

Finally, get the personnel manager's mobile number so that, if anything goes wrong during travel, you can contact him immediately.

3 Joining the Ship

A new Chief Officer joining an unknown ship feels many emotions, among which will be trepidation and excitement. Why not? This is a landmark event in a seafarer's career.

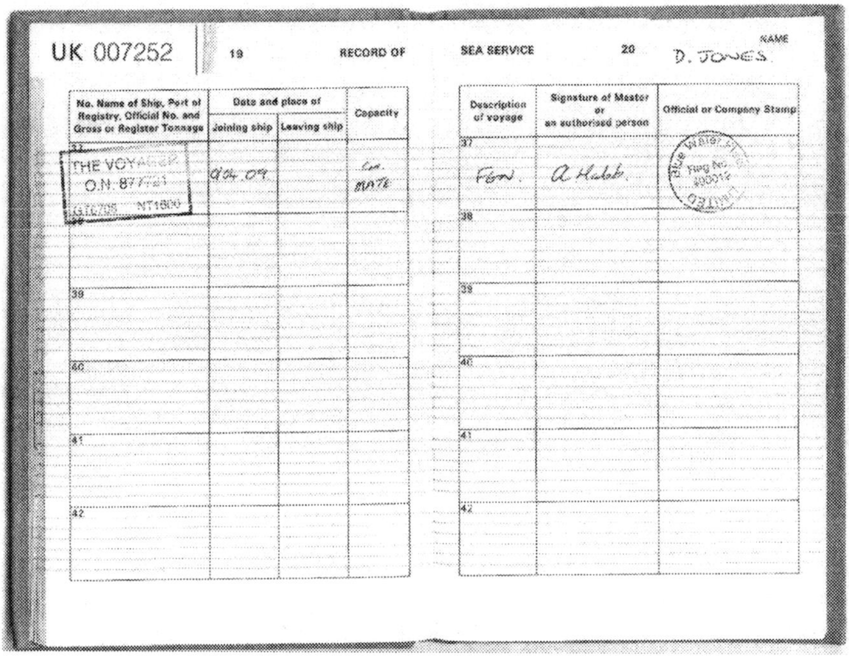

UK 007252 — 19 RECORD OF SEA SERVICE 20 — NAME D. JONES

No. Name of Ship, Port of Registry, Official No. and Gross or Register Tonnage	Date and place of Joining ship	Date and place of Leaving ship	Capacity	Description of voyage	Signature of Master or an authorised person	Official or Company Stamp
37 THE VOYAGER O.N. 877[illegible] GT[illegible] NT1800	9.04.07		[illegible] MATE	FGN.	[illegible]	[illegible]
38						
39						
40						
41						
42						

Discharge book extract.

First ensure that you have a notebook and a good general seamanship book. It is possible that the ship you are joining will have one but you cannot be sure. Also, if you have any sense, you will have asked what cargoes the ship carries and ensured that you have a cargo book that covers them.

On joining, preferably looking like an officer rather than a rating, you should note the state of the gangway, quarterdeck area and accommodation on the way to meet the Chief Officer you are relieving.

If the ship is in the middle of cargo work, particularly loading, any sensible company will ensure that the relieved Chief Officer will remain until the cargo is completed, with you working alongside to ease your way into the system, particularly if you are loading oil, gas or bulk where thousands of tons an hour require constant monitoring of the hold or tank quantities and the continually changing stability. Regardless of the other pressing concerns, the cargo situation must be treated as your first priority and, until you have this under control, don't worry about anything else.

Sometimes you will find the outgoing Chief Officer appearing quite harassed, running around in a dirty boiler suit trying to keep everything going. On the other hand, all could be flowing nicely and he could meet you with a nice cold beer in his air-conditioned cabin while wearing his uniform.

He should take you along to meet the Captain as soon as is feasible. A few things to remember. The fact that the outgoing Chief Officer calls the Captain 'Harry' or 'Attila' does not mean that you can. They could have been sailing together for the last twenty years and be joined at the hip. Call him Captain or even Sir and you cannot go wrong. Once the polite formalities are complete and your documents handed over, move on. This is not the time for any ship discussions, these will come later.

You have a number of questions to ask the outgoing Chief Officer and I suggest that you make a checklist prior to joining. Some of the items you should want answers to are:

3.1 Questions for the Chief Officer

- ❑ Present port problems.
- ❑ The cargo situation, plans and stability calculations.
- ❑ Next port problems.
- ❑ If the stability calculations are on a ship's computer then you will want a run through of this with him.
- ❑ The current ballast system and plan of the tanks.
- ❑ If the ship is a tanker or bulk carrier, you will want a run through of the ballasting system.
- ❑ Enhanced tank survey programme and current state of the tanks.
- ❑ The Captain, his likes and dislikes.
- ❑ Second and Third Mates.
- ❑ The Bosun and the crew.
- ❑ Chief Engineer.
- ❑ Second Engineer.
- ❑ What are the present responsibilities of the Chief Officer?
- ❑ Stores. When is the next storing and current situation?
- ❑ Paint. Is there enough for the forthcoming voyage?
- ❑ Budget. Do you have control of the deck budget and what is it?
- ❑ Expense account. What are you allowed?
- ❑ Surveys. Are there any due?
- ❑ Strange as it may seem, any seating preference in the saloon? Watch for those ruffled feathers!
- ❑ Bridge routine at sea.
- ❑ Dates of wire change and end for end (if applicable) in register.
- ❑ Spare wires for davits, cranes and gangways.
- ❑ Any anchor problems.
- ❑ Pollution. State of hydraulics on deck.

- ❑ If there are hatches, are there hatch rubber spares, tools, adhesive and spare chains?
- ❑ Whether computers are networked and what the passwords are.
- ❑ Fresh water tanks, tonnages and filling rates.
- ❑ Hold damage.
- ❑ Hull damage.
- ❑ Normal sailing trim required by the Master.
- ❑ Periodic tank survey system.

Undoubtedly you will think of more, but the main thing is that you don't think of too many after he has gone.

Ensure that you have all the stability data unless the Class stamped books are with the Master. Also make sure you have sight of the Chain Register (or record of working and lifting appliances) as this belongs to you and is your responsibility. If the outgoing Chief Officer is to remain until completion of cargo operations it will give you time to study the stowage plans and the ballasting systems and ensure that you are satisfied with the departure figures.

3.2 Checking Around the Ship

Having just joined, there are many things going on that will require your attention. However, if time allows, you should take a walk around the ship, examining in particular areas that are your departmental responsibility. You should make your priority those that you can check only while in port. At this stage, you are not looking for a list of faults to be corrected, but rather you are trying to get a feel for the ship and have an idea of your priorities for improvement or change.

You'll obtain a broad overview as you walk around.

3.2.1 Mooring lines

Hopefully these will all be rope as many ports now object to wires. The springs could be wires with nylon tails. Have a look at the general condition of these. Frayed spliced ropes will provide an indication of the company's storing system. Check the wear of the eyes and see if they are covered. How they are secured on the bollards will give you an idea of the seamanship ability of the crew.

A good indication of the quality of maintenance onboard can be found by checking any roller fairleads and whether they turn easily or, as is sadly the case in many instances, they do not turn at all. They are required to turn with pressure from the mooring ropes so if they do not turn they could just be stiff.

3.2.2 Anchors

Are they well greased and are the brakes free from old grease? Are the decks coated in non-slip paint as this is a dangerous working area? Check out the windlass platforms. These can often be corroded and broken in places. The foremast and stays take very heavy weather and a close look at these will give you an idea of the maintenance standard of the vessel.

The working areas of the ship will reveal a lot about how it has been operated.

3.2.3 Foc'sle

The state of the foc'sle will again indicate the housekeeping standards of your department. Chief Officers tend to hoard anything and everything on the premise that one day it might be useful, so on old ships you may find ancient machinery that no one knows the use of, pieces of rope way past their sell by date and drums of obscure liquid with no labels. But at least it should be tidy!

How does the foc'sle store look? Well kept and orderly? Or more like a bazaar or Souk?

3.2.4 Hatch top undersides

If your ship has hatches, this is the best time to look at the undersides. Apart from noting any rust and corrosion, what is most important are the rubber seals around the coamings and any indentations that could stop the seals from being weathertight. If there is any evidence of hatch tape then be suspicious. Hatch tape is fine when carrying certain cargoes, such as grain in winter Atlantic conditions when your ship is trying to emulate a submarine, but it should not be used as a normal sealing.

Any hatches on the foc'sle will be particularly prone to weather damage, regardless of the ship type.

How weathertight is your ship?

3.2.5 Deck lighting

Check these for lamps out, dirty covers and reflectors, and water or condensation inside. You will realise the importance of good working deck lighting if there is ever an accident at night, particularly in port with shore labour involved.

Check the gangway/s and safety net for damage, particularly the platform for any sign of twisting.

How is the means of access?

Finally, have a look at the hull paintwork. Here you are looking for any signs of flaking of corroded plating, oil marks that would indicate a potential pollution problem and to see that the draught and plimsoll marks are clearly identified and that they are in the right place. Plimsoll marks have been known to be upwardly mobile!

3.3 The Bridge

If the outgoing Chief Officer has not shown you around, have the Second Officer give you the tour. Items of importance to you at this time are, the setting up of the radars if you are unfamiliar with the make, the whereabouts of the lighting switch panels, the workings of the engine controls and, if available, the thruster units. All this is particularly important if your station for departure is on the bridge. If this is the case and the bridge is large with considerable equipment that you are unfamiliar with, and you have little time to absorb it, it might be an idea to see the Master and suggest that, as this is your first time on the bridge, it might be better if one of the other officers took over for the departure.

If he agrees you can go forward or aft and the bridge will have an officer who is familiar with the equipment for the departure. Should the Master require your presence on the bridge, it is doubly important that you are familiar at least with the radar, engine controls, communications and, if it is a night time departure, the lighting. Of course, you could have onboard a senior cadet or another deck officer who will be present and can assist, but on many ships this is unlikely.

4 Departure

As yet, you have not had time to put in place your own organisation for running the department, so you will have to go along with what already exists and tweak the system as you go along.

4.1 ETD

When are we sailing Chief?

The first thing to do is establish an ETD. This will normally come from the shore terminal and will be their idea of when they will complete the cargo based on the cargo discharge or load figures. I said 'idea' for, as you know, this is only what it can be. It is not unheard of for a ship to be advised of a specific time for completion only to suddenly be advised that completion will now be several hours earlier or later. Later is no problem but earlier is far more difficult, particularly if stores or repairs have been arranged on the previously advised time or crew have been granted extended leave.

Probably finish at half past...

Consider very carefully the ETD that you are given. Look at your own cargo figures and see if they make sense. Then call the agent and see what he has heard. He will usually get his ETD from the same cargo source as you do, so do not expect this to be very different, but at least you are doing all you can.

Once the time is given the prudent Chief Officer will deduct a few hours to make it an earlier time and make all aware of this as the presently advised ETD. For some strange reason, everyone forgets the word 'estimated' in ETD and, should this suddenly become earlier and they are inconvenienced, it becomes 'you told me this or that time' as if you gave it to them cast in stone. You must live with this. As completion approaches, frequently update the ETD as is appropriate.

Ensure that the gangway board is clearly marked with the ETD and have shore leave expire at least 4 hours ahead of this time. This way you might actually have all the crew onboard in plenty of time, without having to sweat it out as the departure approaches.

4.2 Departure Day

It is to be hoped that you will awake without having been too much disturbed during the night, as you will not be getting much rest today. Once again you will want the latest ETD, and this should now be fairly close to reality. Pass this directly to:

- The Captain
- the Chief Engineer
- the Chief Steward (if you have one)
- the Bosun.

Ensure that the gangway board is updated, once again keeping a few hours up your sleeve for shore leave expiry.

4.3 Trim

You will have calculated the trim required by the Master and the ship should now be almost on these marks. Next ensure that the ship is upright with no list.

4.4 Cargo Completion

The last few hours of cargo work are generally when things go wrong. Everyone is in a hurry. If on a liner schedule, such as would be the case with a container vessel, you are working to deadlines. On all other types of vessels the ports will want you clear as soon as possible. There are other ships waiting for your berth and the charterers or owners will no doubt want you in the next port as soon as possible.

If you are loading a homogeneous cargo, ensure that the last of it is watched and stowed with the same level of care as the previously loaded items. If lashing is required, ensure that this is done properly, not hurriedly. It is better to sail a little late but with the cargo properly stowed and lashed.

Ensure lashings are secure.

At this stage in the proceedings, on a number of occasions, I reluctantly had to delay the sailing of the ship as I was not satisfied with the securing of the cargo or with the trimming of the holds. As the Chief Officer, and being directly responsibly for the cargo, you must keep the Master advised of the situation. Sometimes it is wise to get to him first with your problem as, without doubt, as soon as you state that you are not satisfied others will be hotfooting it to his cabin with their complaints.

You could have a pile of cargo papers waiting to be signed, last stability calculations to do and a draught survey to complete. Therefore, you depend to a great extent on your officers overseeing the decks in these last hours.

Your OOW should be out on deck seeing the last of the cargo stowed and secured, hatch coamings cleared and hatches battened down, hoses disconnected and all the other tasks undertaken that go with cargo completion. You must ensure that, regardless of the time:

- The same attention to cargo is given in these last hours as was given in the first
- the stowage and condition are checked, with any doubts on the OOW's part brought to your attention
- the safety regulations are followed by both ship and shore workers.

Experience shows that this is the time when shortcuts are made and accidents happen. Your ETD will be of no consequence in any court of enquiry.

On completion of cargo you will have your draught checks to make. On large vessels this will have to be completed by boat, provided by the terminal. Don't

Last minute checks......last minute damage!

forget to take the draughts properly with a mean of the highs and lows in choppy waters. Also ensure that the density of the harbour water is checked again as this changes frequently with the tides.

The requirements for securing the cargo operations of the ship depend entirely on the type of ship and the cargo carried. The most difficult requirements are for the closing up of bulk carriers, where the hatch coamings have to be cleared of cargo residue, the hatch tops closed and the same secured with cleats. There will usually be only two hatches remaining, but this can still take time.

The lashings on the hatch top have to be given a final check, particularly those forward. Deck cargo, and heavy lifts in particular, must also be given a final check.

If discharging, the last hatches should be checked for stevedore damage, particularly if heavy grabs have been used. This is not easy on very large vessels because the ship's staff cannot get very high in the holds. It takes several hours to do the job properly and few parties will allow the time necessary.

4.5 Bridge Equipment

If the ship has been in port for some time, ensure that the crew wash down the bridge wings, dodgers and windows ready for sea. In very cold climates with temperatures below freezing, ensure that the heaters are all on. If the windows aren't heated, de-icing should be used on these and on the decks outside.

Ensure that the Second Officer has been given sufficient time to prepare the passage plan for departure.

The OOW will test gear prior to sailing and there should be a checklist for these items. When these have been completed, the pilot card can be made up.

All clocks should be synchronised.

The Officer testing the bridge equipment should report directly to the Master and then to yourself that all the equipment is tested and in order.

4.6 Testing Engines

Engines should be tested in good time before sailing to allow time for dealing with any problems or to give ample warning of any delay to the port authorities. The timing of this should be coordinated between the Chief Engineer and yourself as each department will have its own priorities.

Prior to testing engines:

- Ensure that the stern is clear
- check that the lines are tight

- check that the terminal has been advised and that all the loaders and dischargers are stopped if they are at risk of damage by any movement of the ship
- check that the gangway is lifted clear of any obstructions ashore that could cause damage due to the ship's movement.

4.7 Stowaway Search

Once each area has been searched it must be secured. Areas of the ship that are still being worked will have to wait until the shore labour is clear before they can be searched. The accommodation and engine room will also have to be included in the search pattern. Include all crew cabins in this, not just because a stowaway might have slipped into a cabin, but because it is not unknown for crew to smuggle stowaways onboard, particularly on short sea passages such as in the Northern European area.

The stowaway search is not something that can be done in a few minutes by a couple of the crew. It will involve most of the crew and officers so allow time for this to be done properly. Once the stowaway search is completed, this should be reported to the Captain.

If any stowaways are found during the search they must be handed over to the appropriate authorities.

4.8 Crew Onboard

At the expiry of the shore leave time, you should receive reports from the Chief or Second Engineer, the Chief Steward and the Bosun, that all crew are onboard. If there is anyone missing the Master must be informed immediately. He will then decide what to do. Generally, if there are still some hours to go, he will wait and see. In the meantime, get the Bosun to find out when the missing person or persons went ashore and where they might be.

Do you ever get that 'delayed' feeling?

If after a further hour they are still missing, once again report to the Master in order that he can relay this to the agent.

If they are still missing with one hour to go, then have their belongings packed ready to be landed.

4.9 Securing for Sea

What follows should be the normal procedures for seafarers on any ship about to proceed to sea. However, if you have just joined you will not know the abilities of your crew, the customs of the ship or what has been happening during the port stay, so some of it may not be relevant.

Stow for a hurricane unless you are just port hopping in known perfect weather conditions. Even then the unexpected always seems to happen.

Ahh....a nice cruise down the coast.

Some years ago, a colleague of mine was sailing out of Marseilles in summer, making a short voyage down the coast of Spain to Barcelona. The night after he sailed a storm blew up and he started taking very heavy seas over his decks. His deck cargo of heavy pipes shifted and he took a heavy list. The last that was heard of them was when he advised the situation on the VHF and said that they were abandoning ship in the liferafts. Two days later, three bodies were recovered in one of the rafts. The pipes were stowed and lashed with just chains and no side bolstering fitted, which would have stopped the pipes from shifting.

Check that all cranes and derricks are lowered into their housings and that davits are secure, with the boats stowed up and tight in the davits.

If stores have been taken, have the lockers checked to ensure they are secure, particularly the paint locker.

The foc'sle is a notorious dumping ground onboard, with crew going in and out for various items, so check that all items in this space are secure.

If oil drums are placed on deck, ensure they are placed on dunnage or gratings and are well lashed and not rubbing against each other.

Ensure that all the hoses to the shore have been disconnected.

Finally, after a search to ensure that all shore labour has left the vessel, the final hold hatches and deck doors are to be closed and battened down.

Now you can report to the Captain that the vessel is secured for sea. The agent will probably still be with the Captain so the gangway will have to be left down until his departure.

Find out whether the pilot is boarding by shore or boat and, if by boat, have the pilot ladder or combination ladder rigged ready and clean with someone standing by to receive him and escort him to the bridge.

4.10 Departure

The procedures of unmooring should be familiar to you regardless of the ship. It is important that you realise you are there in a supervisory capacity, regardless of how few crew you have. The idea of you being the officer is that you stand back, give the orders and see that they are carried out in a safe manner. You cannot do this properly if you are driving the windlass or heaving on a rope. Be careful of this one. Mooring accidents are common and if it can be shown that you were not properly controlling the operation, it is your neck in the chopping block.

Normally, if the Chief Officer is not on the bridge for stations, he is on the foc'sle. When unmoored, and if tugs are still fast, keep well clear of the lines. When you are ordered to let the tugs go, if you have tug lines ensure that the lines are slack before letting go and see that they are lowered to the tug rather than just letting them run freely. The tug will often be directly under the foc'sle and, if lines are let run, could fall onto tug crew below. If they are your lines, be careful. All too often the order to let go goes to the tug before you, so the line is released while tension is still on, causing spring back.

Be wary of these dogs of war.

When clearing the port, you will generally stow your ropes away and ensure that those on the drums are tight and well lashed and covered. However, if you are only making a short voyage in good weather and you feel it unnecessary, check with the Captain. Under no circumstances should you leave the ropes out without his knowledge.

As the ship approaches the outward channel, be wary of the speed of the ship and the sea state. You will notice sea state before the bridge, particularly at night, and if the ship is increasing speed into a high swell it is better to advise them sooner rather than later. Every year a number of seafarers are killed on the foc'sle by being swept by seas in exactly such a situation. Meanwhile, as it takes a little time for the effects of slowing down to be seen, clear the foc'sle and have your men move back or stood down.

The Captain may want to keep the anchors cleared away if proceeding in coastal waters. This is sensible, but find out if he wants them 'in gear' or 'out of gear'. I always prefer 'in gear' as it ensures they are not going to run and will only take a short while to disengage, However, if he wants them out of gear, ensure that the brake is screwed up very tightly and that the bars are down.

Make sure that the anchors are hove tightly up into the pipes. Clanging from a loose fluke striking the hull, apart from the damage it may cause, can be heard throughout the ship.

As the poop deck crew will be free well before those forward, I suggest that they be used to check the open decks, clearing any loose rubbish left behind by shore workers or cargo debris that can blow around. Check on the securing of ship's equipment such as gangways and pilot ladders. You may well require to have the crew finish securing the hatches because, while no ship should sail without these being properly secured, there are times when they are half secured and then fully secured as the ship proceeds to sea. You should never proceed to sea with your holds open and, if ordered to do so, it must be construed as an illegal order. More about that later.

If the anchors are to be secured this takes more time, so as the ship proceeds out into deeper waters watch the speed and swell. When the anchors are secured, advise the bridge and wait to be stood down. There are times when you might want to remind the bridge that you are still there. Finally, make sure that the foc'sle weather doors are secured and that the lights are off. Ensure that the bridge has the deck lights on for you as you return to the accommodation.

5 Head of Deck Department

We must first define this role and its responsibilities and boundaries. At times, it may seem that every job on the ship not directly concerned with engines and cooking is thrown at the deck department, and the deck department is also required to do all the watchkeeping at sea and, usually, in port. In other words, it can feel like the most overworked and overstretched department on the ship.

The responsibilities listed are those generally associated with the deck department, but it could be that, in your company there are deviations from this. For example, the engine department might take responsibility for the fresh water or the plumbing. Quite often, individual ships will deviate from the company's regulations if it means the ship runs more smoothly.

5.1 The Ratings

On a ship that has a clear separation between deck, engine and catering ratings, you are in charge of the deck ratings at all times. If the ship has a combined crew, which I have never found works well, you could find yourself generally responsible for all the combined ratings and specifically for their work when engaged on deck duties. Do not complain about this. You will have more experience in dealing with a variety of problems than the engine department, which should mean a more settled crew and it gives you more control over the ship.

The galley, or a hotbed of gossip?

The catering department always seems to dwell on a special cloud of its own unless it is large enough to have a Chief Steward or Purser in charge. If there is no trained Officer or Petty Officer in charge of this department, then it could well be your responsibility as they cannot be allowed a free hand.

Be careful. If there is one man on the ship who is entitled to throw an occasional fit it is the cook, and they are not too respective of rank when they do. Since having one lunatic cook howling around the ship with a meat cleaver in his hand, I have always been very wary of these gentlemen.

5.2 Head of Discipline

Master at Arms?

You are the ship's policeman. Your duties are to see that the company's regulations are followed within the ship and that peace prevails. The level of discipline and punishment will depend totally on the wishes of the Captain and you must seek his guidance at an early stage. Once he passes his wishes to you, it is for you to pass them to the ship, particularly the Bosun, and ensure that they are complied with. The main thing to remember about discipline is that you must remain on top of it.

In reality, punishment exists only as a deterrent, or as a final act if nothing else has worked. We should do all we can to avoid having to take this unpleasant step.

5.3 Second in Command

A big part of this role will be carried out in port during the Master's absence. You will deal with visiting officials and handle their enquiries. It is not your job to just say 'the Master's ashore', as if that relieves you of any further responsibilities. As a manager of the ship there are very few problems that you cannot deal with provided you have access to the various documents that must be presented. It is important that you know where these are and have access to them. If you do not have an office or quarters large enough to deal with official visitors, request access to the Master's office or quarters for this purpose.

What you must remember is that, at all times in the absence of the Master, you must act in the best interests of the company and the ship and with the complete authority of the Master.

5.4 Chief Cargo Officer

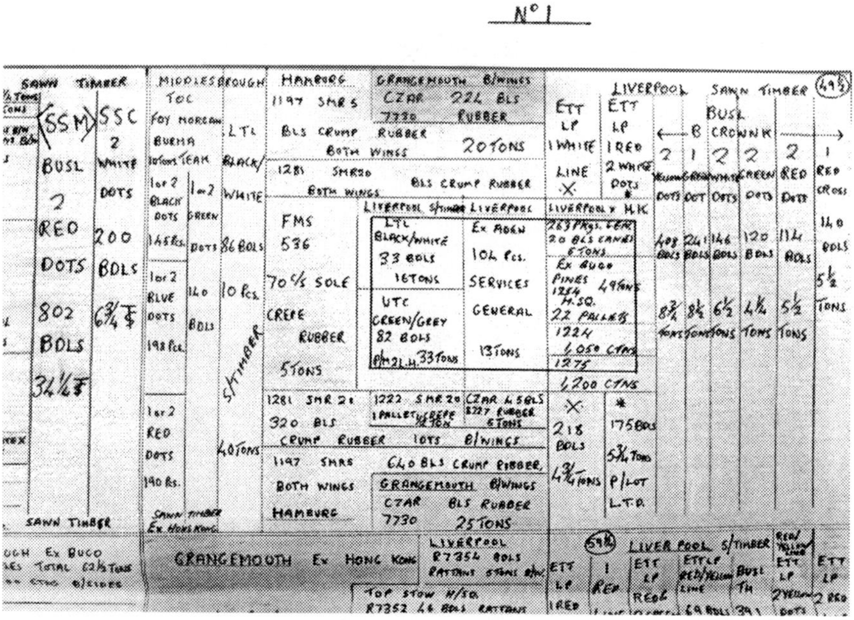

A traditional general cargo plan.

The good old days of the Chief Officer working out the stowage plan and then throwing it at the Second Officer with the words 'get on with it' seem to have gone forever. Now the Chief Officer is expected to stow and supervise all cargo operations in port and deal with all the cargo officials. For passengers, as a cruise ship Captain explained, "use the same principle as for your other cargo. Get it from A to B in the best possible condition".

5.5 Accommodation

All general cabin repairs are your responsibility. This goes back to the days when we had carpenters and plumbers as part of the deck department and, although the work still is there, there are probably no skills left to do it unless you are lucky enough to have a chippie among your deck crew. Hopefully, you are with a company where the plumbing work is part of the engine department brief. However, don't depend on this as it can be a grey area (not just grey water!). You could well be expected to tackle the plumbing problems within the accommodation area, but if the problem is beyond the capability of your crew you will have to call on the engine department.

The fabric of the accommodation could also be within your brief, as could the general cleaning of the public accommodation areas, depending on the size of the catering department.

5.6 Safety

The maintenance of all the ship's safety equipment generally falls to the deck department, and this is sensible considering that the majority of the equipment is in this department. The safety officer might be yourself or one of your officers and so this position is under your jurisdiction. You will need to check whether your responsibility for safety includes all the engine spaces as well, as this can differ from ship to ship and company to company.

5.7 ISM

As the bridge on most ships is also the technical library, all the ISM books and paperwork tends to be there. The responsibility for maintaining these books, informing of any changes and ensuring that the appropriate requirements are complied with as far as possible, will inevitably fall within your department's remit.

5.8 Navigation

Although this is in the hands of the navigating officer, who is normally the Second Officer, as he is your subordinate this is technically part of your department. While the navigation of the ship will generally be between the Captain and the Second Officer, the aspects of bridge maintenance and stores will devolve on you, as will the upkeep of the bridge logbook.

5.9 Medical

Depending on the company, in the past the job of ship's doctor seemed to rest with either the Chief Steward or the Second Officer. With the demise of the properly trained chief steward, it is now firmly within the deck department, with the

Master usually responsible for the safe-keeping of drugs. I suggest that, while this is in your department, it really is the Master who keeps an overall eye on it and unless it is placed in your hands, leave well alone.

5.10 Security

This is the latest workload to hit the ships and, inevitably, the deck department has been landed with it. The amount of work this requires depends on the position of the ship, the availability of personnel and the interest displayed by the Captain. Be careful with this. If you do not have gangway security and a stowaway is found, the blame will be firmly placed with the ship.

5.11 Training

The trainees onboard could be proportionate to the size and number of crew on your ship. The establishment of a proper training regime for trainees will be your responsibility. You must bear in mind that your departmental officers, as well as doing the job they are employed for, are also preparing for their next advancement and so you should also ensure that their coaching and development is considered. Unfortunately, you can too frequently find yourself training officers for the job that they currently hold.

5.12 Entertainment

This might seem like a strange responsibility, but every ship needs some form of entertainment for relaxation. Whether it is organising DVDs to be changed, ordering new dartboards or getting new books for the library, someone has to do it and the deck department is once again responsible. Cadets are very useful for this job.

5.13 Stability and Trim

This is totally yours and usually you are directly responsible for all the calculations. The trim of the ship will be to the Master's requirements.

5.14 Garbage Disposal

Lack of Garbage control could prove costly.

Be careful of this responsibility as while you might not take it too seriously beyond the statutory Marpol obligations, in port others do.

Two incidents spring to mind that I was directly involved in. One was orange peel at the top of the gangway. The coastguard gave us a citation and fine for this and only when we protested that the peel was left by a shore worker and that it was an American orange, did we get this lifted. Who knows if it was, but nothing could be proved.

The second was when a coastguard officer appeared at my office door holding a dripping wet paper menu. It transpired that this menu was lifted from the water near my ship by a patrol boat. After starting to say that this could have come from any ship, I was shown my ship's name, which was on the left hand corner, and the date on the right. Obviously this was now more difficult to talk one's way out of except to say that the wind had blown it out of the saloon and that the menu was paper and would dissolve, and so technically it was not waste. Fined $25,000. That made my eyes water a little and those in the office when I told them. Luckily we were able to negotiate it down to $500.

5.15 Water King

You are in charge of the fresh water and the fresh water tanks.

On ships we often seem to take the provision of potable water on board for granted, only to become disturbed when we see, all too commonly on some vessels, brown water coming from the taps. When loading water from ashore there are ports where we should be more cautious as to what is coming into the ship's water tanks. Equally the tanks must also be clean to receive the water, another novel concept on some ships.

Typhoid fever is an example of a water-borne bacterial infection. The excreta of infected persons could contaminate water supplies. Hence the necessity for safeguarding the water supply for washing as well as for drinking at all times.

Fresh water should be free from causes of infection and be bright, clear and virtually colourless. It should be aerated, that is, it should bubble when shaken, otherwise it has an insipid taste.

Water Testing.

All ships should carry a water testing kit. These are easily available and simple to operate. Many on the market will identify several different contaminates in water such as bacteria, lead, pesticides and nitrates.

Hoses

Hoses intended for loading fresh water should only be used for this purpose. It is best to mark these hoses accordingly and after use, always drain and cap them. The hoses should be stowed away in a dry place off the decks and disinfected every 6 months.

Taking Water

It is recommended that prior to loading water you check the delivery point ashore to see that it is clean. If using a shore hose, then it must be clean and free of leaks as leaks allow germs to enter a hose. If there is any doubt about the quality of the water you are taking then the water must be tested before starting. Water taken from any shore source should be chlorinated.

It is recommended that the section on fresh water in the Ship Masters medical guide is read.

The following recommendations for maintenance of fresh water storage tanks is taken from the template for the MCA MGN guidelines for the supply of food and water on merchant vessels.

Maintenance of Water Systems

Freshwater Storage Tanks

Persons inspecting or working in freshwater tanks should wear clean protective clothing and footwear which has not been used for any other work area and they should not be suffering from any skin infection or communicable disease.

Actions	Intervals
To be thoroughly pumped out and where necessary hosed prior to refilling.	6 monthly
To be opened up, emptied, ventilated and inspected and thoroughly cleaned, recoated as necessary, aired and refilled with clean freshwater chlorinated to a concentration of 0.2ppm free chlorine. The cleaning process should include disinfection with a solution of 50ppm chlorine.	12 monthly
The system (from machinery space to furthest outlets should be charged with super-chlorinated freshwater at a concentration of 50ppm for a period of 12 hrs and then completely flushed out and refilled at 0.2ppm residual free chlorine	Refit or drydock
Pressure Tests on all FW tanks (Subsequent to the pressure test, the system to be thoroughly flushed with potable water.	Intervals not greater than 5 years

Distribution Systems Maintenance

Parts	Actions	Intervals
Filters	Clean Change	Monthly or according to manufacturers instructions
UV exposure area	Clean	According to manufacturers instructions
Calorifiers	To be opened up, inspected scaled and cleaned. Before draining temperaturs should be raised to 70°C for at least an hour to ensure destruction of bacteria which may have colonised the lower and cooler zone of the unit	Periodically (general recommendation - annual inspection)
Shower heads	Particularly in accommodation that has been out of use for an extended period. Clean in a 50ppm chlorine solution.	3 monthly
FW Hoses	Flush and fill with 50ppm chlorine solution and allow to stand for at least an hour before emptying and stowage.	6 monthly or more frequent if required.

5.16 Enhanced Hull Survey

A filthy job that is essential for keeping a watch on the fabric of the ship, this subject is discussed further on in the book.

You can see that everything on and in the ship, outside the machinery spaces and the galley, is yours. There is nothing new in this, indeed it has been the same for the Chief Officers of ships for many years. What is new is the constant loading of new responsibilities, the reduction in your personnel and the removal of skilled personnel. Somehow you will still have to ensure that the most important functions are covered and that the ship is able to perform the purpose for which it is employed.

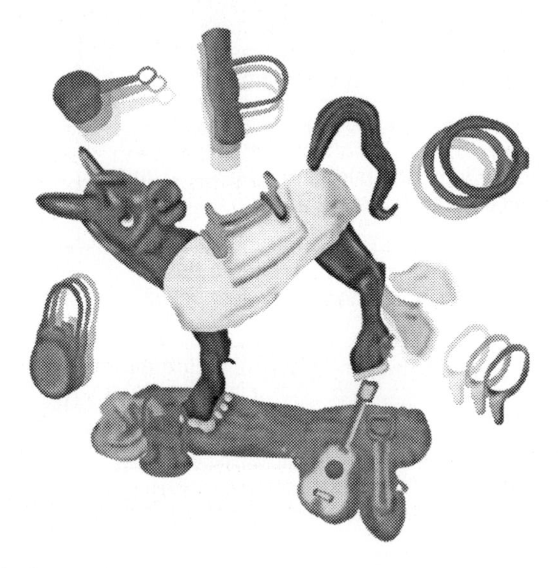

In the words of Star Trek's Scotty, you'll begin to wonder "whether she can take it captain?"

6 The Chief Seaman of the Ship

The basic skill of the profession is not navigation, it is seamanship. An embarrassing word today when, in the defined functions or areas of knowledge for the granting of certificates under STCW, there is no function of 'seamanship'.

So, where and when are we training the modern officer in seamanship? Certainly not in the 4-6 week module at nautical college before you come to sea which leaves the seatime on ships, of which a total of 1 year will be spent before becoming an officer. Of that time onboard, regulations say that 6 months should be spent on the bridge, leaving 6 months to learn the basics of seamanship before becoming an officer. Your time as Third Officer will be spent in dealing with the safety equipment in addition to watchkeeping duties, and as Second Officer your time will be consumed with charts, publications and paperwork, which will leave little time for advancing your knowledge of the practice of seamanship. There are some companies that recognise this as a problem and try to fill the basic gap with their own schemes, but unfortunately such companies are few and far between. On many ships, despite the efforts of those onboard, training is not adequate as trade patterns, passenger comforts (especially on ferries and cruise ships) and the reduced or minimal manning of the ship all restrict what can be done. For these reasons, basic seamanship training, the foundation of the profession, can be sadly lacking and neglected.

6.1 Ship Knowledge

There are two phases of ship knowledge to consider. The first is general seamanship, which is applicable to any ship regardless of type. The second is the ship knowledge pertinent to a particular ship. It will be expected that you have a general knowledge of the cargo systems for the ship you are on. The workings of the hatches, cranes, pumps, anchors and stability should all have been part of your training in the past, both at sea and in college.

In this application of seamanship you could have a problem, particularly if you have been trained in a country with no pre-sea training and you have had little experience on deck as a cadet. This could well have created a considerable gap in your knowledge and, while you may have the theory, you will not have the practice. If this is the case, do not be afraid to ask. You may display your lack of knowledge but you are showing your common sense in dealing with the problem, not causing damage or, worse, endangering personnel by your lack of ability.

The Bosun is the obvious man to lean on and you will not have been the first Chief Officer to throw yourself on his experience. With regard to the practice of the ship, the other officers of your department may have valuable knowledge and this you should also draw on. In fact, it doesn't matter who you ask if it benefits your ability and, therefore, your department and the ship.

Finally, do not be wary of asking the Captain. If you do not know something or have little or no experience of a task or action you are expected to accomplish, then tell him. You might get a scathing remark, but hopefully you will also be told how to do what is required.

Simple rope work can leave a good impression.

Don't forget your seamanship library. This is essential reading regardless of your experience as none of us knows it all. 'Thomas Stowage', Jack Isbester's 'Bulk Carrier Practice' and the many tanker and chemical books that are available are all required for your cargo knowledge. A good seamanship and ship maintenance manual is also essential for your study. Combine the books with the practice, and with a willingness to listen and take advice, and you will get a head start on the path to becoming a competent Chief Officer.

Here is a small tip. If you can do a little fancy rope work or make a good stitch in canvas work, you will be amazed at how impressed the crew can be. You probably know very little about either in reality, but seeing the Mate making a Turk's Head or a canvas cover for a book on the bridge quickly has them spreading tales of your seamanship prowess. It doesn't take long to learn a few seamanship items such as these. Of course, far more impressive would be your ability to inspect a wire splice and, if you are not satisfied, showing them how to do it properly!

Make sure things are done properly.

There are many aspects of seamanship still required, regardless of how modern the ship is. Know what is correct and do not tolerate the incorrect. You know the correct way to throw a heaving line, or should do, so why should you allow a crew member to throw it the wrong way? When lashings are put on, make sure it is in the correct manner. Mooring ropes should be put on the bollards properly. If you have brass on the bridge or in the accommodation then have it polished. If you do not have enough men or time for this, then paint it. Anything is better

than unpolished brass. What I am trying to illustrate here is that you should establish your intolerance of slackness and poor seamanship. Once this is done, you will see a marked improvement in the general aspect of your department and in their attitude to you.

Of course, if you took over an excellent department in the first place, possibly the hardest situation to inherit, then you will carry on maintaining it.

You must read your ship like a book. Just as a book is constantly telling you different things, as a Chief Officer you should notice what is not correct on your decks. A daily walk round in the morning is essential. Just because something was right yesterday does not mean it is right today. With an understanding Captain you might be able to walk round in the afternoon as well, not only to see your ship but to see the work that your crew have been doing.

6.2 Boats and Boatwork

The old adage was that a ship was judged by its boats. Not so long ago, some ships still carried the Captain's gig and he was rowed ashore in places like Aden, showing off the smartness of the boat and crew. Agencies in places like Hong Kong also competed in the appearance of their boats. Ships and their crews' abilities can no longer be judged by such displays or even the outward appearance of the ship. However, the good order of the boats and the crews' ability to use them is still vitally important.

The maintenance of the lifeboats and rescue boat, if you are fortunate to have one, must always have priority over other work. If your Captain allows them to be lowered to the embarkation deck at sea, that is excellent. Many do not or the company regulations state that this is not to be done. This puts pressure on your schedule in port as that is when these boats must be lowered.

Permission to launch boats must be obtained in most harbours and I would make a point of automatically asking the Master to request this in every port, provided you are not port hopping once a week or more. Either way, you should aim to have one of your boats in the water at least once a month and a boat lowered to the embarkation deck at least every two weeks. This is for you to decide and, out of courtesy, advise the Master of your intentions, particularly if you are the safety officer. Think of your job as being to ensure that the Master has his boats well maintained and in good order, with a crew well trained in launching them and in the use of them.

Enclosed lifeboats can only be used in calm conditions in harbour or you may never get them back. For stern launched lifeboats there is now a tendency to recommend not launching for exercise. This is nonsense. Of course they have to be exercised and the crew launched in them to give confidence in the boat and its abilities in case the necessity arises for doing it for real. I used to launch these regularly in harbour without any problems.

If you have a rescue boat it is essential that it is exercised regularly with the same crew. You will have crew who are supposed to have been trained in its use, but be careful here. The training that they have received is very basic and carried out in calm conditions. Choose the crew with care. Those who are in the crew, and the minimum is three, should have received basic training in the use of the rescue craft. Apart from that, it is useful if they can swim as this will give them more confidence in the boat. It is essential that you have first-hand experience of their abilities and this can only be achieved by you going away in the boat with them. Regardless of your experience, they will look to you for guidance in boatwork because of the assumption that you cannot have been promoted to Chief Officer without having acquired a reasonable knowledge of it. This, as you know, is not so if you come from a nation that has abandoned pre-sea training. If this is the case, and you have junior officers that have had this training, you might be better off asking them to assess and train the boat crews.

Either way, your crew must be capable of taking the rescue boat away in a seaway and somehow you are going to have to achieve this. At least by regular boatwork they will gain confidence in their abilities and in the skills of lowering the boat, taking it away and recovery. Ensure that at all times when the rescue boat is used the crew are wearing their survival suits and inflatable lifejackets and that they have full communication with the ship.

With regard to the lifeboat/rescue boat, this is a different matter. While you must exercise them in still harbour conditions, it is not possible to exercise them in a seaway owing to the difficulty of recovery. At times you will find recovery in the harbour difficult enough. What could save you considerable problems is having rope pennants that can be used to hook onto the falls and onto the boat, so the boat can be recovered using these without the difficulty and dangers of having to engage the falls directly onto the lifeboat. The lifeboat can then be hung off when up in the davits and the falls re-engaged.

It was thought that an engineer should always accompany the lifeboat when it was sent away, but this is not necessarily the case. All crew should be able to operate the engine and there is no reason why one of the deck or engine ratings cannot be trained sufficiently well to operate the engine correctly. After all, the engines are no different to those on thousands of leisure boats and those owners do not seem to have too much trouble!

Take time to examine the lifeboats for getting stretchers inside and for adequate ventilation. Many of them fill with engine fumes if the doors are secured, which they have to be in heavy weather. Also, it is very probable that the engine noise prohibits communications inside and the engine controls cannot be reached by the coxswain. Some of the designs are atrocious.

Although the boat is equipped with oars, it is most likely that these cannot be used properly through the ports provided in the hull as quite often they will have to be put into the holes from the outside and the draught of the boat makes the oars' angle of entry into the water too steep to be effectively controlled. Have the crew try to use them and then at least you will know if they are useless.

It is wise to know the limitations of your boats before you have to use them for real.

6.3 Boat Maintenance

While the maintenance of the boats will be listed in the maintenance schedule, the specific crew members doing this maintenance are not. Considering the importance of these boats to you, I suggest that you consider ensuring that the same crew members are responsible for doing this task. There are solid reasons for this. They become familiar with the boats and the equipment and they become more responsible in their work ethic if they know that they can be held to account for any deficiencies. In addition, an officer should frequently inspect the boats, a good time being at the regular boat stations when the officer can give instruction in the equipment and its use to assembled crew.

Ensure that there is an established routine for running up the engines of all your boats regardless of type and, if you carry spare outboards, the same must be done for them.

Don't forget your battery checks, every week without fail.

Your lifeboats will have oars and in open boats these can be used, with crews exercised in this. These are also provided for enclosed boats, which is a bit like providing sails for your ship. Even so, they must be maintained and this means occasionally oiling them, especially in open boats where they are exposed to the sun. Make sure that your rowlocks are still in place on their chains. These chains are subject to rust and may need replacing. From experience, rowlocks without chains disappear.

6.4 Boat Stores and Equipment

The boat stores have to be checked frequently, particularly the favoured theft items. Pilfering from the boats goes on not just from the shore workers but from your own crew. Stupid as it may seem, even the ships on standby and rescue in the North Sea, where the men absolutely depend on the fitness of the boats, encounter this problem.

It is tempting to lock the access if it is an enclosed boat. I agree that this is a good idea in port but, if it is done, you must ensure that the boats are immediately unlocked on sailing.

If you have open boats you may believe that all the stores should be removed to a nearby locker. However logical this might sound, you cannot do this or accept it being done. The boats are required to be instantly ready day and night, and that means that all the required stores have to be in place. The open boats should not be covered. I know there are many reasons why a cover seems a good idea, but I assure you the delay in getting the covers off on a stormy night could mean the difference between getting off or going down with the ship. If you do have covers, while you keep them off at sea, they can be put on prior to arrival in port.

For some strange reason, while the regulations require us to have fishhooks in the boat, boats are not designed with a toilet and there is no mention of sick bags or lavatory paper. In the average enclosed plastic boat, after a few hours, things are going to be extremely messy, particularly in high seas. With no bilges there is the question of what we are supposed to do with our waste matter, but meanwhile it might be an idea to ensure that each boat at least has a supply of lavatory paper and bags.

7 Steel Preparation and Paint

But what lies beneath?

There are many tasks that involve your crew onboard the ship, but preparing surfaces for painting and the painting itself are probably the largest. The problem with painting seems to be in the preparation, with the occasional Captain, Superintendent and company wanting the ship to be painted 'now', regardless of the time taken to prepare the steelwork. This is why, too often, rust is painted over and, even in dry docks, ships' hulls, tanks and holds are painted before they are dry or in poor weather conditions, often against the recommendations of the paint manufacturers, with a resultant quick deterioration in the paintwork and the steel it is supposed to protect.

7.1 Costs

Paint and coating costs vary widely. The cost of repairing non-performing coating systems in service can be high, and quite disproportionate to new build costs.

The following are estimates from Safina Ltd:

The cost of coatings and their application may typically represent:

- 0-5% of total ship cost at construction for commercial ships
- 0-15% of total ship cost at construction for chemical tankers
- 5-15% of annual maintenance costs for commercial ships
- up to 50% of dry docking costs for large ships.

7.2 Surface Preparation

Too often, the surface preparation is a compromise between what should be done and what is possible with the small number of crew on the majority of ships. Unfortunately, if the surface preparation is not carried out correctly, the painting that follows will be more for cosmetic appearance than for the protection it is primarily intended for.

The surface being painted must be clear of all rust, dirt, oil, grease and salt. It must be completely dry. Without this, the paint cannot properly adhere to the surface and fill all the pores of the steel. There are a number of solutions on the market for the cleaning of surfaces, but care must be taken that very strong cleaning agents are not used on existing paintwork as they tend to burn or soften the existing coating. Thinners are commonly used to remove grease and oil but, if these are used, the surface must be washed clean afterwards.

7.3 Hand Tools

Wire brushes are good for cleaning out pitted surfaces, welding areas and light rust and paintwork. Scrapers are useful for dealing with small areas where power tools cannot be used.

Chipping hammers, the traditional basic hand tool of the seas, still have their uses but these must be used with care as too heavy a hand can dent the steelwork. Once dented the metal forms a high and low area, which means that the paint will follow such contours with the thinner paint on the high area. This will wear off more quickly than in the thicker area and will leave spots of rust that will spread under the thicker areas.

7.4 Power Tools

Increasingly, power tools are replacing manual tools and, without a doubt, their utilisation improves steel preparation provided they are used properly.

7.5 Blast Cleaning

This is the most effective method for preparing steelwork for painting. Before blasting the surface must be free from grease. It is better to grind down any rough edges, such as welding seams, prior to blasting.

The surface obtained during blasting depends on the grade and type of abrasive used, the air pressure and the skill of the operators.

On many ships, for economy, reuse of the abrasive is required. This can only be done with good quality abrasive and the second use will never provide the quality of blasting obtained on the first run.

7.6 Paint

The primary purpose of paint is to seal the pores on wood and steel, decreasing the decay and the formation of rust. By smoothing out the surfaces, it provides a washable surface and a pleasant appearance to the overall finish.

7.7 Types of Paint

The metal of a ship is subject to differing environments. The bottom part is rarely dry, the middle sections of the hull are constantly changing from wet to dry in seawater, and the topsides are frequently subjected to differing temperatures, wind and weather. Each area requires differing preparations and paints designed with the properties best suited for the area it is to be applied to.

Bottom paints

These paints rarely affect you as Chief Officer as they are normally applied in dry dock by shore personnel. However, it is important that they are applied correctly and you should watch for this in the dry dock. These are anti-fouling and anti-corrosive paints with the anti-corrosive being applied first.

Anti-corrosive

Anti-corrosive paint contains heavy pigmentation and requires frequent stirring as the pigmentation tends to settle in the bottom of the drums. Without this pigmentation, the effectiveness of the paint is reduced. It also dries very quickly in comparison to other paints. It is essential that this coating is properly applied and covers all the bottom as the next coating of anti-fouling paint can cause pitting if it comes into direct contact with the steel.

Anti-fouling

This paint is used to prevent the fouling of the ship's bottom, as this reduces the speed of the ship and increases the fuel consumption. Copper oxide is the chemical that has been the most effective in dealing with marine growth, and this is applied over the anti-corrosive paint. However, with the introduction of the new IMO Convention on the 'Control of Harmful Anti-Fouling Systems on Ships', which was adopted in 2001, the present day effectiveness of anti-fouling on ships will decrease, with a subsequent rise in fuel costs or reduction in speed.

Under the terms of the Convention, by 1st January 2008, ships were not '*to bear such compounds on their hulls or external parts or surfaces; or shall bear a coating that forms a barrier to such compounds leaching from the underlying non-compliant anti-fouling systems*'.

They are used to reduce the consistency of the paint to assist its application. However, they also reduce the ability of the paint to penetrate the surface being covered and they reduce the 'gloss' effect. If paint is thinned too much its protective nature will be reduced.

Primers

Primers are rust inhibitors that are applied as base coats onto prepared bare steel. They seal the pores of the steel and provide a smooth surface for the top coats. Normally, at least two coats of primer are used before applying the topcoats. On aluminium and galvanised steel, only zinc chromate primers should be used.

7.8 Painting

The following guidelines for paint application are reproduced with the kind permission of Jotron Paints (Europe) Ltd:

1. *All equipment should be clean and checked to ensure it is in perfect working order and is the right equipment for the job.*
2. *The correct type of paint must be used and it is important to carefully follow the specification for the actual area to be painted.*
3. *Read the instructions on the Technical and Safety Data Sheets, observe the safety precautions and do not smoke whilst painting.*
4. *Avoid inhaling solvent vapours. Ensure there is good ventilation if working in an enclosed area.*
5. *It is always advisable to wear goggles, mask and gloves. Always wash your hands with a hand cleaner or soap and water.*

   Do not use thinners or solvents to clean your hands.
6. *Before painting commences prepare a plan of how the tins of paint are to be distributed over the surface. Separate the area to be painted into reasonable sections and distribute the paint tins accordingly. This method helps to achieve a more even distribution of paint over the entire surface and ensures the quantity of paint corresponds to the specification.*
7. *Paint must be thoroughly mixed otherwise the quality may not be as expected. This is essential as the heaviest pigment in the paint sinks to the bottom of the tin.*
8. *Adhere carefully to instructions regarding the potlife (that's how long before it becomes unusable).*

   Potlife decreases as temperature increases and vice versa.
9. *Avoid unnecessary thinning. In cold weather it is advisable to keep the paint at room temperature.*

10. *Measurement of temperatures must be carried out in the vicinity of where application takes place.*
11. *When painting, the temperature of the substrate should be a minimum of 3°C above the dew-point to avoid condensation.*
12. *Follow the instructions regarding the recommended spreading rate for the paint.*
13. *Check the drying times, what may appear to be dry may not be. The ideal temperature range for applying paint is between 15-25°C with humidity at 85% maximum. Outside these ranges the drying times will be affected.*
14. *Paint should never be applied to a wet surface or during rain. Avoid painting when it is windy and avoid direct sunlight. Don't paint late in the day, remember evenings and night time are when moisture forms.*
15. *Sacrificial anodes must be replaced. It is essential that new anodes are not painted and it is advisable to protect them with aluminium foil. Tape may also be used. Remember to remove the foil or tape after painting. Additional cleaning may be required.*
16. *The wet film thickness must be measured at frequent intervals. The recommended thickness must be maintained throughout the painting.*
17. *The drying time between each coat must be in accordance with the current Technical Data Sheet for the product.*
18. *On Technical Data Sheets a typical dry and wet film thickness is shown. This is normally only achieved by airless spray application. To obtain the recommended dry or wet film thickness by brush or roller, the number of coats needed may at least need to be doubled.*

Prepare the area properly. Grease spindles to keep the paint off. Paint is not meant to go onto rubber seals as it hardens and prevents the rubber from sealing properly and also degrades the rubber. Ensure that sealing tape or grease is put on windows and portholes.

A problem area is cable trays, which are usually made of cheap metal that rusts and then streaks down onto the paintwork. There is really only one thing to do with these, which is to carefully take the cabling off and strip and prime the runs properly before replacing. If you have these old metal ones onboard, then replace them with plastic ones.

Have the crew go round and scrape the paint off all the places that they should not have painted, such as the windows. If they realise that they will have to do this every time they are careless, you will be surprised at how their painting improves.

If you are spray painting, ensure that the crew take the basic precautions, which are:

- If painting in well ventilated spaces or outside, a dust cartridge respirator can filter out particles of paint effectively, providing the cartridge is replaced at regular intervals
- if ventilation is poor then it is essential that a proper air fed hood and masking system is used
- under no circumstances are rags or cloths tied over the mouth and nose to be used. These do not filter the paint properly and the rags can become impregnated with paint particles and allow the paint into the mouth.

Finally, pick your time and place for painting. I had the whole and bridge front painted in gleaming gloss white off the Namibian coast heading north. Then we ran into a sand storm. The result was a pink front that felt like sandpaper. Unfortunately, pink was not the Captain's colour.

7.9 Safety Precautions for the Paint Locker

Most paint presents a safety hazard, both to the ship and to the health of those working with it. Precautions that should be taken are as follows:

- All paint, thinners and varnishes are to be kept in sealed containers
- if canvas or other material is used to protect the deck, this must be taken up at the end of the day, removed and dried out. Leaving it in the locker could cause spontaneous combustion
- used rags should be kept in a metal container and disposed of once work has finished each day. These rags should not be left in the locker overnight.

The immediate problem to health are the vapours emitted by the various paints and coatings and clothing that is paint splattered. By sealing the containers and changing clothing, this danger can be removed.

8 Ropes and Wires

Regardless of the type of ship you are serving on, ropes and wires are part of your daily existence and, if outside the engine room, they are your responsibility.

Using the correct cordage in the proper way and the inspection of this is essential. Too many lives at sea are lost by the abuse of wires and ropes and the failure to inspect and replace defective items. Most heavy work ropes at sea are Manila, sisal, nylon or polypropylene, and the chart below provides a comparison.

	Nylon	Polypropylene	Manila
Strength*	1	3	4
Wet Strength vs. Dry Strength	0.85	1	1.15
Shock Load Ability*	1	2	4
Floats or Sinks in Water	Sinks	Floats	Sinks
Elongation at Break (Approx.)	20% - 34%	15% - 20%	10% - 15%
Water Absorption	0.06	0	1
Melting Point	480°F	330°F	Does not melt Chafes at 350°F
Abrasion Resistance*	2	4	3
Degradation:	Good	Poor	Good
Resistance to Sunlight			
Degradation:	Excellent	Excellent	Poor
Resistance to Rot			
Degradation:	Poor	Good	Poor
Resistance to Acids			
Degradation:	Good	Good	Poor
Resistance to Alkalis			
Degradation:	Good	Good	Poor
Resistance to Oil and Gas			
Electrical Conductivity Resistance	Poor	Good	Poor
Flexing Endurance*	1	3	4
Specific Gravity	1.14	0.9	1.38
Storage Requirements	Wet or Dry	Wet or Dry	Dry Only

*Ratings: Best - 1, Poorest - 5

8.1 Manila Rope

The main problem with Manila rope is that it has to be stored dry, which causes difficulties if it is used as mooring rope and has to be stowed below in a wet condition. If this occurs the line should be flaked down, if possible, to give it the best chance of drying out. Other problems are that it is heavy, particularly when wet, and does not float, requiring more manpower in handling.

Deterioration of the rope is indicated by a discolouration from yellowish white to grey, although to distinguish this from surface grime the inner part of the rope has to be inspected. A further indication of deterioration is bristling ends of broken yarn, and rope that is overstrained will show a decrease in diameter. Natural rope when overstrained will give out cracking noises and wet rope can show a steamlike vapour. All of these signs indicate a line that is in danger of breaking. In normal usage natural fibre rope deteriorates by around 30% in two years.

8.2 Sisal Rope

This is again a natural fibre rope, considerably cheaper than Manila and therefore often used instead of it. It has about 80% of the strength of Manila and lasts about the same time, although it is easily damaged by continuous exposure to weather.

8.3 Nylon Rope

Of the synthetic ropes, nylon is the best. It is more expensive than Manila but lasts longer and, on an equal diameter, is 3 times stronger, It is impervious to weather and can be stowed away when wet as it does not absorb water.

It is particularly good for mooring lines and any other use where limited shock is required as it stretches up to 30% of its length under normal working loads without any degradation of the line.

Similar to Manila rope, nylon rope when under strain emits cracking noises and can also show the same steam-like vapour when wet. Synthetic rope should always have more turns put on bits than natural fibre rope as the friction ratio is less. While all rope under strain should be kept well clear of, nylon rope in particular must be treated very carefully because of the severe backlash on breaking, with the rope possibly stretched to up to 50% of its length at this point.

8.4 Polypropylene Rope

This is cheaper than nylon rope, does not stretch as well and so produces more shock. It is not as strong but it does have some advantages in that it floats and is lighter than a nylon rope of equal diameter, so is easier to handle. It is more susceptible to damage from sunlight though and should be kept covered when stowed outside.

8.5 Wire Ropes

Wire rope consists of a number of strands laid helically around a supporting core. Individual strands are composed of a number of wires laid helically around a centre (core) of wire or fibre. The lay of a wire rope is defined by the direction in which the strands are laid into the rope, and by the direction in which the wires are laid into the strands.

Regular Lay Rope	Lang Lay Rope
In regular lay, strand lay direction in the rope is opposite to the wire lay direction in the strands. Regular lay is preferred where additional resistance to crushing, rotating or distortion is required	In lang lay, the strand lay in the rope is the same as the wire lay direction in the strands. Lang lay ropes deliver maximum flexibility and resistance to bending fatigue and abrasion.

Right Lay Rope	Left Lay Rope
In right lay, the path of the strands runs left to right as shown. May be either regular or lang lay.	In left lay, the path of the strands runs right to left as shown. May be either regular or lang lay.

8.6 Wire Rope Cores

At the centre of every wire rope is a core, usually made from either wire or fibre. The core acts as foundation for the strands, keeps the rope round and provides clearance between the rope strands for unrestricted movement.

Ropes with fibre cores have greater elasticity, but metallic cores afford greater strength and resistance to crushing.

The following different kinds of wire rope cores are available: Independent Wire Rope Core (IWRC), wire strand, Manila fibre, sisal fibre or polypropylene. Under normal operating conditions, a fibre core provides fully adequate support for the strands and acts as a reservoir for the lubricant. Wire cores are usually composed of a separate 7 x 7 wire rope, termed Independent Wire Rope Core (IWRC). In any case where heavy loads or over-winding on a drum will cause excessive pressure of strands against the core, the IWRC is a necessity.

8.7 Uncoiling

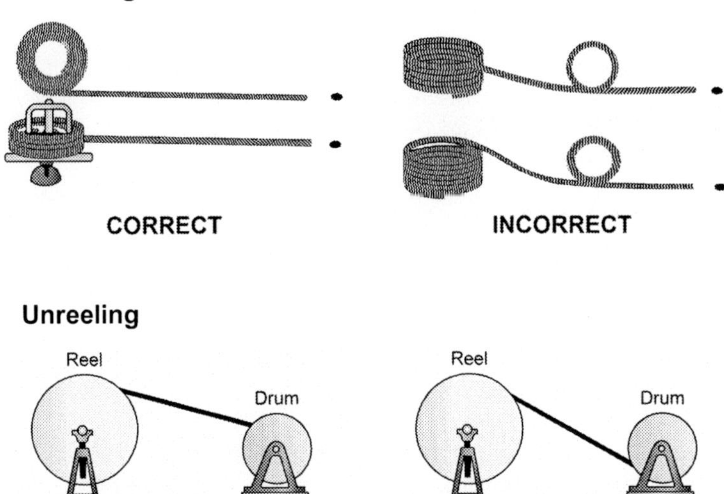

8.8 Handling

Upon receiving a shipment of wire rope, close attention to the packaging is the first important measure in proper and appropriate care. If, for example, the reel has broken or split flanges or loose inner sleeves, it is a fair assumption that there could be damage to the rope as well. Always check for distortions in the outer wraps of the reel or any conditions resulting from forklift abuse.

8.9 Care and Inspection

Wire rope is subject to the same wear and tear of all metals at sea. If the diameter of the wire is decreased it is an indication that the wire has been under strain for a prolonged time. A good indication of deterioration of wire rope is broken wire strands standing proud of the wire. These are commonly called fishhooks as they can rip open an unwary hand or, if wearing gloves, can catch on the glove and drag the wearer's hand into a block or drum.

To prevent corrosion and rust the wire must be lubricated regularly. Some wires are galvanised to prevent rusting, but in this process the strength of the wire deteriorates by up to 10%.

9 Heavy Weather

Was everything secure last night when you finished up for the day?

Sometimes at sea, particularly if you are constantly trading in more northerly latitudes in winter, the ship will sail into very heavy weather. Hopefully there is some advance warning of the oncoming situation and so time to prepare the ship. As the Chief Officer, the main responsibility for carrying out these preparations is with you. If you have a Master experienced in the weather patterns of the part of the world you are in, he will undoubtedly direct you to the precautions that are required.

However, it could be that direction is not forthcoming and so you are required to consider the situation for yourself. It is important that you make sure you know the rudiments of preparing a ship for any weather situation.

9.1 At Sea

You must assume that the main brunt of the weather will be taken on the bow. This is because of the sensible anticipation that, when the weather becomes really bad, the Captain will put the ship's head into the sea. So concentrate here first. Make sure that your anchors are completely secure, stoppers and claws are on, the hawse pipes and spurling pipes are covered and cemented or foamed and your ropes are stowed below. All this should have been carried out as part of a normal departure from harbour, but it does no harm to repeat the checks required.

When stowing your ropes, lash the ends together so that when you stow them down you have only one end left, which you can secure to the underside of the hatch. When you need to bring them on deck again open the hatch, take the end and heave all the ropes out together, one after the other. It saves a lot of time.

With regard to the hatches on the foc'sle, cleats on and tight is not enough. The seas can knock them loose and smash the hatch open.

This happened to me in the North Sea, and the fore part of the ship was flooded in a storm at night.

There are two ways to secure these hatches. The best way is to tack weld. Then, when you want them open again, just use a hammer to knock them free. The other way is to rope the cleats together, weaving a rope web so they are all secured to each other. Sometimes a net is put over the hatch to achieve the same objective. In addition, the weight of your mooring rope secured on the inside hanging down will also help keep the hatch secure.

Your vents should also be covered and the covers firmly lashed down, although quite often in a severe storm they will disappear. Plastic bin bags, which can be seen on some ships, are really not suitable for this and it is why you still need canvas at sea and seafarers who can work with it. Make sure that your halyards are tight and the stays on your foremast tightened up. Remove any loose gear, even wooden platforms for the windlass.

Now the foc'sle store. This always seems to be the ship's junk room and plenty of the gear in there is not properly secured. You really do not want loose gear, particularly drums rolling around, so again secure it, and especially the paint store if it is here. Secure down the weather doors, hammering the cleats home.

Similar checks follow on the main deck. Ventilators, hatchways and masthouses should be secured down and loose gear removed, stowed and secured. Ensure that all your safety lines are rigged and tight. If you have cargo hatches all the crew must go round each hatch and tighten the hatch top cleats, with special emphasis on the forward hatches.

If you have an amidships pilot ladder make sure this is inboard and well battened down, similarly the main gangway. The poop area must have the mooring ropes completely secured if they are not stowed down, both with lashing and canvas covers. Check whether the Captain wants the deadlights put up on the main deck. The further forward your accommodation, the more likely it is that you will need deadlights. The side ports below the main deck should certainly have deadlights secured.

On the boat deck, check the boats are secure and there is no movement in the davits, then work your way up to the monkey island. Ensure that the top of the magnetic compass is well secured and the covers are lashed down and that all the halyards are tight and well secure. All the main deck accommodation, weather or storm doors must be secured and dogged down, except for one door on the lee side on the main deck that can be lightly dogged for easy exit.

Have the furniture in the messrooms and smokerooms secured and the table fiddles up in place. Finally, check the storerooms as the catering department never seem to realise that they work on a ship that tends to move!

9.2 In Port

Do you have enough lines for the forecast weather?

In port there is a limit to what can be done to safeguard the ship. As Chief Officer, you are responsible to the Captain for ensuring that his requirements are carried out and for suggesting any further precautions that might assist with the situation. However, if the weather has suddenly worsened and the Master is not onboard, the situation is entirely in your hands.

The first thing to verify is the direction of the wind. Is it blowing you onto the berth or off it? Onto the berth is preferred as at least then your moorings and the security of the ship alongside is safe. In such a case your one concern is any ranging that the ship might do along the quay, and any damage that might be done to the hull and coatings by the fendering. You should ensure that your moorings and springs are tight enough to stop this and that the gangway is watched carefully for any damage. If necessary, try to put out any additional fendering that you might have onboard. You must remember that if the wind is blowing you onto the quay, it could also be forcing the water into the harbour and onto the berth and there could be a rise in the water level.

If the wind is such that it is blowing the ship off the quay then, on any warning of the worsening weather, you should increase your moorings. If the ship is relatively light, see if you have time to ballast her down. As in most cases ships break away from the berth in the fore part first, you should consider lowering the outboard anchor onto the bottom. This will assist considerably in holding your bow in.

This hole was left by a bollard that had five headlines secured to it before the wind rose to 60 knots and blew the ship off the berth (breast lines on self tensioning winches did not help matters either!)

Watch the cargo operations. If the ship is moving at the berth and the port has not suspended cargo operations you might have to consider stopping, particularly when working with light or wind susceptible loads such as empty containers, timber or similar. In many ports the limit for crane and loader operations seems to be a maximum of 40 knots, with some ports it can be much lower.

Sometimes terminals can be reluctant to stop work just because you consider that the operations are becoming too dangerous. This is a difficult situation because if you stop them working when they do not have the same opinion you could find that the charterers claim the period as off-hire. There could also be a threat of being thrown off the berth. Such a decision should rest with the Captain but, in his absence and as the ship's cargo officer, if you consider that the ship could be damaged by the terminal's continued operation, and if after discussion with the terminal supervisor he continues operation, call the agency runner down to the ship and put in a note of protest to the terminal. At the same time move the ship's personnel away from the endangered area of operations.

The most effective way to stop terminal operations is to close the hatches or stop the pumping of cargo. Because of the possible consequences of such actions, you should do this only under the most extreme circumstances if you do not have the authority of the Master.

You should advise the agent and see if he can contact the Captain to let him know of the deteriorating weather situation, although if he is in the vicinity he will observe the weather deteriorating and will probably be returning to the ship already.

You should stop all shore leave for the deck department and consider sending them to stations to standby the moorings. An additional precaution is to have the engines put on standby.

If you become more concerned about the movement of the ship, call the harbour and request a tug for standby.

10 Freezing Conditions

Account for ice allowances.

It is not my intention to go through all the problems that ice can cause, particularly when deliberately entering ice on ice class ships. As a Chief Officer, if you are appointed to such ships then you should have had ice experience in a more junior capacity and there are excellent books available on the subject of ships in ice, such as the 'Ice Navigation Manual'. Normal vessels will also encounter freezing conditions, particularly when venturing to the northern ports of Europe and Asia, and the cold conditions experienced can cause severe damage to the ship. Even as far down as Hamburg and the North Sea, ships have been badly affected by freezing temperatures.

If you are going into such areas in winter, and there is a chance of you encountering freezing conditions, there are certain precautions that you should consider taking.

10.1 Preparation and Precautions

The following items are to be checked prior to entering ice or carrying out ice operations:

General

- ❑ Check the inventory of cold weather gear onboard and replenish any deficiencies

- ❑ if the ship is not fitted with double glazing, perspex or cling film placed over windows can help insulate the accommodation
- ❑ examine towing fittings on the foc'sle and ensure that a suitable messenger is available to pick up a bridle or towline
- ❑ ensure regular monitoring of the water level in all spaces and compartments. This could be as frequently as hourly in areas of heavy ice concentrations. This should also be instigated after a strong ice impact
- ❑ searchlights fitted and tested
- ❑ pilot ladders should not be lowered too early as ice can accumulate from spray
- ❑ ship's hydraulic systems filled with a fluid suitable for cold weather operations, ships fitted with tunnel thrusters should not use these as they are liable to damage from ingested ice, which could damage the blades.

Deck Service Lines

- ❑ Isolate and drain the following lines, leaving the drains open
- ❑ fire mains. Valves must be left cracked open
- ❑ general service line and fresh water line to all deck outside taps
- ❑ deck air line
- ❑ chain locker eductor
- ❑ anchor wash lines
- ❑ winch cooling lines
- ❑ all external taps
- ❑ drain bridge window wash systems unless antifreeze has been added
- ❑ be alert for the formation of ice at any overboard discharges.

Whistles

- ❑ Drain main and forward whistles and close drain cocks.

Safety Gear

- ❑ Stow forward liferaft and LSA gear
- ❑ stow deck foam and water fire extinguishers in heated areas
- ❑ stow lifebuoys.

Lifeboats

- ❑ Drain fresh water tanks
- ❑ ensure potable fresh water tanks are full and located in a warm room nearby
- ❑ fit lifeboat drain plugs
- ❑ Consider the addition of:
    - Sets of sub-zero temperature insulated clothing (S, M and L sizes) including hooded jackets, trousers, gloves and boots
    - sets of thermal underwear and socks
    - sets of face masks and goggles
    - sleeping bags (down filled)
    - Arctic type igloo shaped survival tents

- additional high energy food supplies, such as chocolate bars.

Grease

Grease should be applied liberally to all the moving parts on the decks including:

- Windlasses
- mooring winches
- cargo winches
- engaging clutches
- pins
- operating handles
- brake clamping bolt threads
- all nipple points
- sounding pipe cap threads
- hatch dogs
- davits
- cranes.

Note: A little anti-freeze is effective when mixed into the grease.

Halyards and Stays

- If halyards are left up then they should be slacked down.

Protection

- Covers off all searchlights
- covers on hatch control boxes
- covers on all fire hydrants
- covers on all fire hose boxes
- covers on all mooring lines on drums, leaving lashings clear before making fast to enable release
- covers on bunkering sounding pipes
- grease and burlap (hessian) hatch drive motors and gypsies.

Heaters

- Foc'sle fan and space heaters switched on
- winch hydraulic header tank and hatch hydraulic heaters switched on
- anti-condensation heaters on hydraulic systems switched on
- winch, hatch pump and exhaust fan motor heaters switched on
- any deckhouse space heaters switched on
- fire pump and davit heaters switched on
- space heaters in emergency headquarters switched on.

Additional Items for Tankers

- Decontamination showers and eyewash stations to be accessible to crew in all weather conditions
- drain foam lines

- ❑ cargo heating coils either to be empty or steam to be circulated
- ❑ aft peak tank to be heated, if ballasted
- ❑ pressure vacuum (P/V) breaker to have the correct amount of anti-freeze (glycol)
- ❑ steam to be opened to deck water seal and cargo oil pump separators
- ❑ crude oil wash (COW) lines and COW machine stand pipes to be drained
- ❑ P/V valves to be operated to ensure free movement
- ❑ insulate lines from cold with a trace-heating system. Care should be taken that thermostats are functional and have enough power to run through cables to provide effective trace-heating.

Tankers – Cargo Heating Systems

If cargo heating system is not required:

- ❑ Drain/blow through inlet/exhaust lines to remove all presence of water

If cargo heating is required:

- ❑ Introduce steam to the cargo heating system before encountering freezing temperatures
- ❑ consider fitting a small diameter line (jumper line) between the supply and return manifolds on the forward tanks to prevent freezing of the exhaust returns
- ❑ test all steam and exhaust valves for tightness so as to prevent leakage into 'dry lines'
- ❑ maintain heating until ship reaches warmer climates
- ❑ blow through all coils/lines with air immediately after turning off the steam.

Additional Items for Gas Carriers

- ❑ Drain both deck water spray/sprinkler lines and safety relief valve drains
- ❑ drain both safety relief valves and vent masts
- ❑ cargo heaters and cargo condenser fresh water cooling systems to be kept on
- ❑ emergency eye wash and decontamination shower lines and tanks to be drained
- ❑ attach and post a pipeline drawing of the number and location of the drains and indicate which drains are to be blanked and drained. The same should to be clearly marked at their location
- ❑ isolation valves of lines to be posted and clearly marked at their location if space heaters are not provided. Cluster-lights may be safely rigged close to the machinery and electrical panels and kept on.

Note for Dry Cargo Ships

Ships regularly trading in ice should carry a long-handled blowtorch fired by propane and a sufficient stock of cylinders should be maintained onboard.

10.2 De-Icing Tools

Courtesy Stena Bulk

Have equipment and machinery prepared.

If you take freezing spray on your decks the ice will build up very quickly. To work the ship, this will have to be cleared from areas such as the windlasses, doorways, etc. This will have to be done manually. Steam lances are used in some circumstances, but the problem with these is that the steam can freeze as it leaves the lance, adding to the problem rather than helping. Shovels are essential for removing newly fallen snow before it freezes on top of that already there. You will have to ensure that you at least have a path along your decks for personnel to move around. Ice can be knocked off using wooden mallets and pickaxes and crowbars can be used with care. This equipment should be stowed in an enclosed space, such as the foc'sle or aft store, to be ready for use. When working on deck in the ice, care must be taken of ice falling from the rigging and masts. Much of this can be shaken off by hand or with mallets.

De-Icing

If you do not have heated bridge windows or blown hot air systems, you must have a good supply of de-icing sprays. If you have bridge wing controls, keep the dials free of ice with the sprays.

Anti-freeze

Anti-freeze must be used in all the boat engine cooling systems.

Scuppers

Clear the scuppers of the grilles so that when freezing water is taken onto your decks, it can run away freely. Insert rubber hose piping into the scuppers so you can remove it when the pipes are frozen to give you ice free scuppers that allow water to run away.

10.3 Crew Clothing

It is essential that the crew have suitable cold protective clothing to wear and that spare clothing is carried to replace wet gear. Winter weight padded boilersuits, padded work gloves and winter boots must be supplied. Liners for hard hats, with ear coverings, must be fitted. It is important that frequent breaks are given and that there is always an adequate supply of warm food and drinks. Thermos flasks are very useful when securing or letting go as these actions can be prolonged in ice conditions.

10.4 Damage Control

Although you will not generally be navigating in Arctic waters, there is a possibility that you will find yourself in waters with ice.

The IMO 'Guidelines for Ships Operating in Arctic Ice-Covered Waters' state:

> *All ships navigating in Arctic ice-covered waters should be adequately equipped and their crews properly trained to provide effective damage control and minor hull repair.*
>
> *Damage control equipment should, in accordance with the above, be sufficient to enable a ship, as far as practicable, to make temporary repairs to a minor hull breach or to take precautionary measures to prevent escalation of damage or flooding, so that the ship may proceed to a location where a more substantial repair can be affected.*

Not many crews are trained in damage control, particularly on ships that only occasionally transit ice waters. On modern merchant ships the equipment for damage control of the hull has generally been discarded on the premis that the majority of hull damage suffered will be so large that the crew could not attempt temporary repair.

However, ice provides a totally different scenario, While catastrophic damage can still result, about which the crew can do nothing, there is a very real possibility of damage below the waterline being small but still capable of allowing water to jet into the ship. The smaller the hole, the stronger the force of water. While the pumps could probably cope with the water flow any such ingress is bad, regardless of where it is and regardless of whether or not the pumps are coping. However, if the hull penetration is in way of the engine room this could cause damage to the machinery and/or electrics that would render essential pumps inoperative and leading to, in an extreme case, the loss of the ship.

There are a number of temporary damage control devices that seem to have come from a bygone age, but that could still prove very effective.

The first are wooden wedges, both flat and pointed. If a box of these is kept in the engine room, and any other strategic place required during ice transit, they will be ready for instant use.

The next is a rigid bottom weighted large canvas or tarpaulin square, with ropes attached. If this is stowed in a locker on deck, it will be ready to be thrown over in the area of damage. The weighted bottom drops the square down in the water alongside the hull and the force of the water entering the ship drags it towards the damage, forming a cover over the hole. This will not stop all water from entering, but the force of the jet will be reduced substantially, enabling those inside to take more effective action and providing temporary respite. The difficulties of getting wedges in against the force of the water and working with ice cold water flooding over the bodies of those attempting repair must also be remembered.

In the damage control inventory on warships there is a piece of equipment called a splinter box, which comes in different sizes. It is a dome shaped device with rubber seals around the rim and a long screw with a folding bar device through it. The long screw can be pushed through the wedges or canvas and then, as it is screwed, the bar opens to form a crosspiece to hold the cup while it is screwed tight and in place.

Perhaps consideration should be given to making such equipment a standard requirement for ships navigating in ice.

In 1999, I encountered damage from ice on the bottom of the ship - it was only a small penetration but it had to be dealt with. The Chief Officer and I entered the DB for inspection and used wooden wedges to stop the flow of water. Then the crew put a cement box over the hole and all was well. What was interesting was that we were able to identify the hole not only from the sound of water spurting in but from the light beam coming from the hole, which was rather surprising considering that it was on the bottom of the ship.

10.5 Cargo Work in Ice Conditions

Make sure cargo gear is working before you arrive.

A few last points if you are to work cargo in cold weather. Hydraulic oil has a lower viscosity in cold weather, which means that the colder the weather gets the thicker your oil becomes. Therefore, if you do not have heaters for your hydraulic system, switch the motors on well before they are needed. It is always embarrassing to get alongside and not be able to open your hatches, and even more so when you are put off-hire.

If you have a build-up of ice or snow on your hatches, try to get this off before opening them as weight puts severe strain on chains and hydraulics. If the hatches are iced up and beyond your ability to clear before getting alongside, notify ahead to the agent for a de-icing company to be ready for your arrival.

11 Relationships

Take care what you say as sometimes 'sorry' may not be enough...

11.1 You and the Company

Your main contact with the company will be with the visiting personnel of the company to the ship. Courtesy and politeness are always to be afforded as with any visitors, but remember that they have no formal authority on the ship and cannot give any orders. If they do you may have to politely remind them of this, particularly when dealing with superintendents. Company officials who know the ropes will understand this and good superintendents will request that something is carried out through you.

If you have a definite complaint regarding the company or your treatment by it, then voice it. Provided this is done in a polite and reasonable manner, there is no justification for anyone to resent it. However, if the matter concerns the ship or those on it make your complaint onboard first.

Be circumspect when you are asked about the Captain. This question should never be asked about a superior but many company officials do. Do not be flattered at being asked as whatever you say will be used to their own purposes, which may not always be good, so keep your mouth firmly closed. If there is ever the unfortunate time when it should become necessary to speak out against the Captain, then let it be your choice and choose who you speak to unless, as happened with me, it is an official inquiry into your actions.

11.2 You and the Captain

Your relationship with the Captain is dealt with in Chapter 12.

11.3 You and the Chief Engineer

This can be a problem for the Captain, never mind you. The Chief Engineer wears four stripes and you wear three. Therefore, he is the superior officer, which is perfectly acceptable. However, you are both heads of department and so are equal in responsibility.

Quite often you will be asked to work with the Second Engineer. This should be no problem as such arrangement for the daily work makes sense. But some take this further, requiring you to deal with everything through him and feeling that to deal with you on equal terms is to lower themselves. I emphasise that this is only some. You cannot accept this and you must politely continue discussion on subjects that require his knowledge or cooperation, or if they are things that he should know about. If he is older and possibly wiser than you, throwing in the odd 'sir' will not go amiss. It cost nothing and shows your respect for rank and seniority. If you do not know something regarding deck machinery or on any other aspect of the ship, do not hesitate to ask him. After all, if he knows the ship or company well he can be of great assistance. Do not discount the Chief Engineer's knowledge of seamanship either. Quite a few of them have been many years at sea on different ships and have seen far more of the sea than you. I had the pleasure of sailing with a number of Chief Engineers who would come on the bridge for departure and arrival and regularly took an interest in the navigation of the ship. They can be very useful mentors to young inexperienced Chief Officers and, on occasion, inexperienced Captains.

Keep him advised of your work programme, particularly if it involves power as extra generators might have to be used, and of the cargo schedules.

You should not be intimidated by the Chief Engineer or allow your department to be harassed. There may well be times when you will have to stand up and be counted. Provided this is done properly and not in anger, any ruffled feathers can quickly be soothed.

11.4 You and your Deck Officers

As the Captain will depend on you, you should be able to depend on these officers. Your greatest problem will be to have them accept responsibility and make decisions. Unfortunately, very few will be used to this so any problem, regardless of how small, may end up on your desk and nothing will happen until you make a decision.

There are many reasons behind this. Companies have become increasingly reluctant to accept that even you can make decisions, never mind your officers. Captains and Chief Officers, perceiving a deterioration in the abilities of the junior officers, have taken more responsibility onto themselves to ensure the job is being done properly and to protect themselves.

Your officers do not know you, and what you want from them, unless you tell them. The art is to be able to tell them in a way that will achieve their cooperation. If you can, try to establish a bond between you, rather than an austere approach. Friendship and cooperation should be the aim. First-name terms are fine, not just between your department officers but with all the other officers as well. You will want every officer's cooperation at some time or other.

Keep the officers advised about what is going on and the reasoning behind your actions. They must be able to feel that if they have any problem, at any time, your door is always open. In this way you establish a bond while still establishing respect for your authority. The occasional informal discussion over a glass or two does not go amiss either.

Tell them of your attitude to discipline and what you expect from them in this regard. Make sure they know that they can rely on you for your support and assistance at any time.

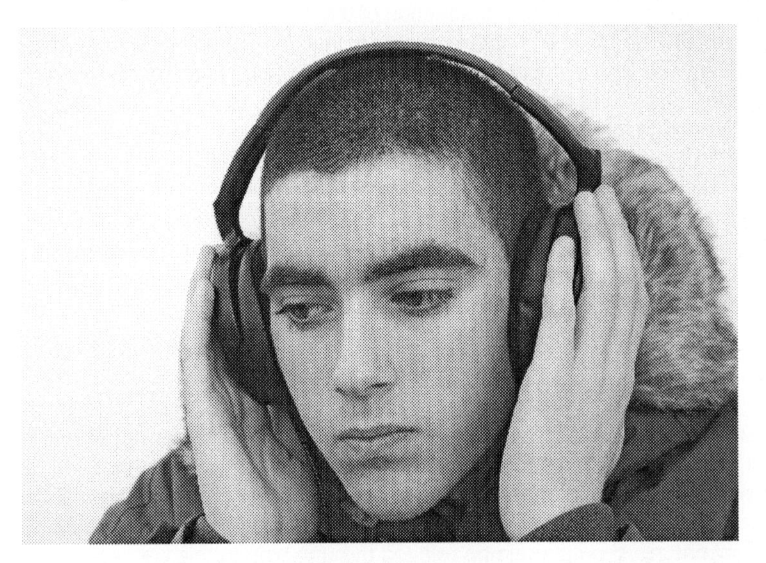

You may think that your junior officers are like unruly teenagers.

You could well find that your officers are not of the professional standard that you consider appropriate. This is difficult as there are now many junior officers at sea who haven't progressed through the system in an ideal manner.

This is not necessarily their fault and they may share your opinion that their standard or training is inadequate.

You are not going to change the industry and, unless the officer is particularly bad, if you have him replaced the chances are you will not get any better, possibly even worse. Ask yourself a few questions. Can you work with him? Apart from his lack of knowledge or intelligence, does he work hard and does he try to please? Does he carry out his orders? Will he listen to you? If you can answer yes to these questions then the chances are that, with patience, you can accommodate him and hopefully raise his standard.

On the other hand, if you have an officer who is professionally incompetent and despite your efforts there is no improvement, you must bring this to the Master's attention and request removal. If you are certain that this is the only correct course, then put this in writing to the Master with a copy for yourself. You are taking these actions for a number of reasons. First, it is your duty to all onboard to see that the officer is removed before any serious incident ensues. Second, you are protecting yourself because should something happen as a result of his incompetence and you have not brought this to the attention of the company through the Master, you will be apportioned blame. Another reason is that you cannot, on a busy ship, afford to carry anyone who is not pulling their weight. Those days are gone forever and if someone is incapable of doing his job it will fall on you to take up the slack. You are not paid enough for that!

Finally, the crew will know of his incompetence and will have no respect for him. This also means a loss of respect for you, as this is your department. Crew seeing an incompetent officer 'getting away with it' will question why they are bothering to do their own job correctly. This is not ideal even in normal situations, but, in an emergency, there could be serious consequences.

11.5 You and the Bosun

The Bosun is the senior Chief Petty Officer of the ship and your right-hand man on all matters regarding seamanship and the crew. It is essential that you respect his position on the ship and support him at all times. All orders to the crew must go through this man and all crew complaints and problems, unless they are of a personal nature, should again be relayed through him. In this way you enhance his status among the crew, particularly when they see that he is in such a position of trust. The Bosun must equally accord you the same respect. It is quite in order to ask the Bosun about any aspect of the ship or even seamanship that you are not familiar with. He has spent longer on deck than you did in your training and should, therefore, know a great deal more than you about the practical aspects of seamanship.

The Bosun is your link with the crew, their general attitude and any particular problems.

A certain familiarity can exist between the Bosun and the Chief Officer, to the extent that they can achieve an 'understanding' of each other and work together for the benefit of the ship. A weekly meeting in the Chief Officer's cabin to run through forthcoming work and any problems can be very useful.

Having said that, remember the Bosun is not always right, particularly when it comes to crew relations. After all, he is not a trained personnel officer and neither are you. If anything goes wrong, you are the one who carries the can so, while you listen to the Bosun, keep the other ear open.

11.6 You and the Crew

The crew will vary with the type of ship. On short sea trades and ferries and in the oil support industry, with regular leave and short contracts, a more regular crewing can be achieved with the same crews rejoining, so a familiarity with the ship and each other can be established. In many cases a sense of propriety can exist and, though many would deny this, a sense of pride in the ship. All of this can assist the Chief Officer in the day-to-day running of his department. The downside, however, is for the newly joining Chief Officer in being accepted as the new 'man in charge' and in making any changes to the existing systems. Crews in such a position tend to become very entrenched in their practices and lifestyles onboard and any new Chief Officer must proceed with care when changing them. Tread softly. If you want a change in some working practice, explain why you think that this is necessary. Then acknowledge your willingness to change back if the new way does not work. If this can be established, and you seem a reasonable man who is not just making change for change's sake, then you can proceed, hopefully without any active opposition, and your change will have a good chance of succeeding.

The crew on most larger ocean going ships are a mixture of nationalities, religions and cultures, all with different reasons for being at sea. For many of the younger ones, it is to escape poverty back home and support families. Many will, when their houses are built, their taxis bought or other businesses established, leave the sea with elation. Few have any desire or reason to remain. For the older ones it is often because they have nowhere else to go. With such a mixture, it is difficult to infuse enthusiasm into the work. The ship is just another ship, they rarely know the company they work for, you are just another Chief Officer and this is just another day less before they go on leave. Sounds depressing doesn't it? But for many crews life onboard is depressing, especially on old ships with long empty alleyways, empty cabins, deteriorating accommodation that no owner is interested in upgrading as the ship is old, and a ship that is gradually declining with not enough crew or materials to cope.

11.7 Confidential Reports

As the Chief Officer, along with the Chief Engineer, you will have the responsibility of writing reports about the officers and crew in your department. You will submit these to the Captain, who will add his comments or discuss changes he feels necessary with you, and then he will submit them to the company. He in turn, when the time comes, will write reports on yourself, the Chief Engineer and the Purser if you have one.

The importance of these reports is somewhat open to debate. They should be important and used both to the benefit of the person and the company, but too often they become only of use to the company and then only used during times of plenty. Many Captains, Chief Engineers and Chief Officers have submitted quite dreadful reports only to see the same officers and crew reappearing on other ships in their fleets. However, your SMS will state that these have to be completed and therefore they must be done. Some companies require them to be submitted at periodic intervals and want you to read the report to the person being reported on. This is no problem if the report is good but can cause considerable problems if it is not, especially if that person is resentful at what is being said. That resentment can turn to anger and unpleasantness onboard, usually directed at the officer doing the reporting. Imagine a Captain submitting a bad report about a Chief Engineer and that officer remaining onboard for another three months? Such a situation could be very unpleasant for all.

A system I have seen incorporated is to submit a report during the voyage only when extreme circumstances require it, and that this would lead to the removal of the person being reported on at the first opportunity. Otherwise the normal reporting system is used and a report submitted when the officer or rating completes their contract and is leaving the ship. This system is adopted by more sensible companies and at least ensures that they get a far more truthful report and have a better picture of their fleet.

In making your report, if you are with a company that acts on them, then you have a duty to take care with what you say and to ensure that you are not biased by any personal feelings. If you have to submit reports periodically and read them to the person concerned and you are making an adverse report, I suggest you discuss the situation with the Master first. He could well decide to change it anyway.

12 The Chief Officer and the Captain

The ultimate relationship between the Captain and the Chief Officer can be summed up in simple terms. He makes the big decisions, you make the small ones. He takes responsibility and gives you authority. He gives you trust, you give support. You both respect each other.

A matter of trust.

This relationship is important enough to warrant its own chapter. The Captain is head of the ship and the superior officer to all onboard. That is the law. It is the traditional and the only way a ship can proceed on the sea. Merchant ships are not part of a military organisation, but military discipline at sea historically stems from merchant ships as they were the first to sail and fight on the seas.

12.1 Support

Ships, whether tugs, tankers or cruise ships, by necessity require a structure of discipline and order to survive. As the Chief Officer you are a key figure in that structure. As the Captain's right-hand man and the designated second in command of the ship, your support for the Captain is critical to good order and morale onboard.

You might feel that it is rather strange that you, as a newly promoted Chief Officer, are expected to support a possibly quite experienced Master, however the support is not necessarily in knowledge but in your manner. There are occasions when the Master might not be too popular onboard for a variety of reasons. While this might cause friction within the ship and add to your concerns, you must support visibly and verbally the authority of the Captain regardless of others' views. As the Chief Officer, you will find that there are those who wish to involve you in their complaints regarding the Captain. Be very careful of this. Under no circumstances should you involve yourself in these matters as that, in their eyes, makes you one of them. There is an easy solution when this starts. Simply tell them to come to the

Captain with you and state their case openly rather than moaning behind his back. That usually deals with the situation and lets them know where you stand.

12.2 Advising the Captain

Where & when?

Even the most senior Master sometimes finds that another opinion can be helpful, provided it is expressed properly. There will be times when the Master will ask for your opinion but, on other occasions, you might feel that you should speak on a matter you are concerned about. Provided this is done with courtesy you are doing your job. The bridge is where you should feel free to state any concern you may have with the Master's actions and, in fact, you have an obligation to do so.

Some years ago, on a very fine and sunny day, a passenger cargo ship belonging to one of the UK's best companies was steaming along towards a rock, some miles off of which the ship was to alter course. The rock was perfectly visible to all and had been for many miles. On the bridge were the Captain, who was a Senior Master in the fleet, Chief Officer, OOW, Senior Cadet, Quartermaster and lookout. The Captain had the con. The ship arrived at the alteration point but the Captain said nothing and carried on closer, but still no alteration. No one else spoke. Eventually the ship ran out of sea, and made a perfect landing directly onto the rock at full speed, proving the old adage that if your draught exceeds the depth of water, you are aground. The Captain turned to those present, when they had picked themselves up, and declared that it was his entire responsibility.

But he was wrong. The OOW should have expressed his concern. The Chief Officer should also have stated his doubt regarding the navigation of the ship and, as the rock got closer, expressed it forcibly. This would have been an occasion to have directly interfered and ordered the immediate alteration.

The only time I ever did this was not on a merchant ship but on a Royal Naval vessel. I was the OOW and we were going through the Pentland Firth in very bad weather with the ship pounding severely. The gyro went off line and the Captain, who had just arrived on the bridge, became confused and gave an order that put the ship directly heading for the rocks. I immediately countermanded his order and ordered the wheel the other way. There was what we should call a 'small altercation' between us and then he realised what he had ordered and was extremely grateful for my interference. I was extremely grateful I was right!

If you are to be the right-hand of the Master, then you must tender your advice when needed and sometimes when it might not be needed, but you feel the situation requires it. In this way, you are doing your job and assisting the Master who will hopefully recognise this, if not at the time, maybe later on reflection of the incident.

12.3 Second in Command

For you to properly fulfil this capacity you need to know what is going on and it is up to the Master to keep you advised of any general affairs that affect the running of the ship. Theoretically, he should discuss with you any decisions he makes relating to the ship and tell you his reasons, particularly if you have to implement them. He should also show you all the mail from the company that concerns the ship or those onboard except any that refers to confidential matters. In this way you know what is going on before being told about it in the galley by the cook.

Prior to arrival in port, if there is not an arrival meeting the Master should go over all the events taking place during the ship's stay in the port and you should advise him of your intended cargo and department operations during the stay. In this way, should he go ashore you are able to act for him in his absence.

At sea, if the Master is incapacitated in any way, you will again act on his behalf until he is able to carry out his duties. This is a little different from formally assuming command. There might well be an occasion when you will need to do this, with the permission of the Master, and unfortunately times when you will do this without his permission owing to death or a serious impairment.

If the Captain has failed to return to the ship and this has been reported to the operating office, you might be ordered to assume command. Congratulations! On the other hand, in the event of the Captain suffering a serious illness and being unable to make decisions or receive your reports, you must then decide to formally assume command until relieved of responsibility by the Master returning to health, or being relieved by another Master appointed by the company.

For this you will make an entry in the ship's logbook and you should have the Chief Engineer and Second Officer witness it. Be very careful that you discuss the situation with these officers beforehand and they understand the reasons why this is being done. People have been accused of mutiny for this action, a word that seems very archaic in this day and age but that is still on the statute books.

Here is a report I personally had to make against accusations of taking over the ship and acting against the authority of the Captain.

'On sailing from Durban, the crew were in a very unsettled mood after the Captain banned all shore leave, while going ashore with his friends during the entire stay. Shortly after departure the Captain began drinking heavily, failing to write the night orders or visit the bridge, instead taking to locking himself in his cabin. During this period we received the first warnings of the approach of tropical cyclone Honorine.

After making the plot of the probable track of the cyclone, it was obvious that if we kept our intended course we would enter the area of the storm. I took the plot to the Master's cabin and he said that we would wait. From then on he lost interest, although I advised him of the position of the storm and its approach as the reports came in. As the weather conditions began to deteriorate I made one further attempt to persuade the Captain to take action, but without success. At this time I also had to take the Second Officer, the Second Engineer and the two cadets to the crew quarters, where there was a gathering of crew members intending to enter the officers' quarters and demanding to see the Captain, who was in no condition to see anyone. The crew dispersed but it was obvious that the situation was serious. Accordingly, with the agreement of the Chief Engineer and the executive officers, I assumed command of the vessel making an explanatory entry in the Logbook. As there was now no way for the ship to avoid the cyclone, with the weather constantly worsening, speed was reduced and the head put into the sea. The storm passed within 18 hours, causing slight damage to the tarpaulin hatch covers on No 1 and No 2 hatches. I kept command of the vessel until shortly before arrival at Dubai, when I handed command back to the Master, who had now left his cabin and come onto the bridge.'

The report goes on but you get the general picture. I am pleased to say that on the day of enquiry on the ship, the Master was so drunk he could not stand and had to be carried off the ship, which exonerated me and closed the enquiry.

Hopefully, you will never have to take such drastic steps and your situation as second in command will be the supportive role it is intended to be. But there are times when incidents do occur and you have to be ready. The sudden transition from your role as Chief Officer to temporary command can be difficult for some to understand, particularly when it is a situation, for example, in port when the Master is ashore and decisions have to be made and orders given. It is obviously far better if you can request people's cooperation and they respond realising the necessity of what you are doing. On the few occasions when this is not accepted and your requests are questioned or, worse, refused, then you have no alternative but to give a direct order, with a witness. This might make the dissenter realise the seriousness of your intent but, even if not, you will at least have a definite accusation to make regarding a serious offence and one that could have dire consequences should damage to the ship or injury result from such a challenge to your authority.

12.4 Keeping the Captain Informed

Jungle drums are very effective in a confined environment like a ship.

Captains find out what is happening on their ship in a variety of ways, not least through their own sense of mood of the ship from their years of experience. In addition, there are always sources of information from others onboard who are not averse to telling the Master what they feel he should know, from their own point of view of course. From you, however, the Master should be able to rely on getting truthful information, even if it is not good news. If the Master feels that he can rely on you for this you will find that his trust in you will grow, and that will benefit both you and the ship. There are times when there are things that it would, at that time, be better for the Master not to know. For example, if the Master is a strict disciplinarian who goes by the book, and your very good and competent Third Officer went ashore in port and returned late for his watch, you are perfectly capable of dealing with this. So why tell the Master and escalate the problem? You have dealt with him and presumably the problem will not occur again. Case over and finished. It is in certain matters like that where you can exercise your judgement. It may be that the Captain will know about it anyway and, if he asks you, you can simply say that it has been dealt with.

The Captain should come to rely on you for the general mood and opinion onboard, not radio galley.

Hopefully the Master will have an established routine where he will either come on the bridge during your morning watch, or you will go to his office after breakfast, or you will catch up at morning coffee. Anything relating to the wellbeing of the ship should be discussed at that time. If there is anything of importance you must be able to advise the Master at any time.

12.5 Running your Department

The Chief Officer is head of the deck department and I would advise that if you find yourself in any company that tries to say differently then you should seriously consider your future with them. This is not just because of any degrading of your position onboard, but because this position is an essential step in your preparation for promotion to Captain.

Most Captains are happy to let you get on and run your department without interference unless they are unhappy with the way you are doing things. The most difficult situation is where you have a newly promoted Captain. Until very recently, he was doing your job. Now you arrive, possibly newly promoted to your rank, and he has to stand by and watch. This is not easy for him, particularly at the beginning, and a certain tolerance is required from you with regard to his suggestions and ideas.

There is interference, and there is helpful assistance. The first you don't need and the second is very useful. Interference is where you have a Captain who goes onto the decks and gives orders to the crew rather than giving them through you or discussing them with you first.

One Captain did this with me. I was ashore, it was raining heavily and he had been advised that some of the office managers were coming to the ship. He was one of those who panicked at the sight of office personnel and he ordered the crew to paint the side of the ship where it had rust stains. The hull was white. From morning to late afternoon all the crew, over the protests of the Bosun, painted white paint over the wet hull. You can imagine what happened, the paint ran down onto the green boot topping and, when the management arrived, they were most dismayed at the mess of the hull. Unfortunately, he then told them that I had ordered this! Luckily, the Bosun told them in no uncertain terms who had given the order.

If you do have a Captain who wishes to run the department then you have no alternative but to let him do it. However, don't let him run all of it. A colleague of mine, when he was Chief Officer, ordered the crew to remove everything from his office and put it all in the Captain's office, including all the cargo and stability documents. This initiated a decision by the Master to sit down and discuss the situation, which was resolved to my colleague's satisfaction.

Generally, not many Captains want to run your department. It is just that they say and do things that affect your control without considering that it could be interpreted as interference. If there is no justification for this then a quiet discussion of the problem will, in most cases, resolve it. He is not a mind reader and you will most probably have to initiate the discussion.

On the other hand, if you are not running your department to the Captain's satisfaction he should discuss this with you before it goes too far. He is in command of the ship and, regardless of your opinions, your department must be run the way he wants it.

12.6 Managing your Captain

Be careful that the tail doesn't start wagging the dog!

If the truth be known, most Captains enjoy being managed by a competent Chief Officer. It is pleasant to have your day managed onboard, to be told by the Mate that all is well with the world and that all is secure in his hands. With this trust, the position of the Chief Officer grows and he is able to take on more authority. As I said at the beginning of the book, the Chief Officer is the day-to-day man. When he goes to the Master's office or cabin in the morning and advises the Master of the training drills that he intends holding, what repairs will be effected and any meetings that he has organised, the Master gains an impression of efficiency in such a confident approach. To have a Chief Officer with such capability and confidence is the average Master's dream. If you achieve this stature, be careful. No one will want to promote you and lose your abilities!

Remain aware of where the ultimate responsibility lies.

Regardless of your confidence, you always have the Captain to fall back on. You can finish your watch on a particularly stormy night, write up the logbook and happily go to your bunk leaving him to worry about the ship. Any problem you have can be placed before his desk and all final decisions are not only his prerogative, but expected of him. He has the authority and you use this on his behalf, as long as he wishes it to be so.

On arrival in port however, the situation changes a little in respect of the cargo for which you are, in all practical ways, responsible. When things go wrong it is the Captain that has to answer and appear before any hearings. It is understandable then that many Captains are a little nervous over the cargo operations, particularly with a new Chief Officer, and this is why you keep them advised of anything that might be problematic. On the other hand, for the experienced Chief Officer, a Master who wishes to also oversee the cargo can be, to put it bluntly, a nuisance.

One peaceful day on the Malaysian Coast, just as I was thinking of a lunchtime gin, there was a commotion from one of the hatches and, on arriving there, I found all the labour streaming out of the hatch and work stopped. On enquiry, it appeared that a large cobra had decided to take up residence in the hold. One would have thought that they would have been perfectly used to snakes but obviously this was not the case, so the cadet on watch was ordered forth and, armed with a boat hook, told to enter the hold and dispatch the snake so that work could resume and I could have my gin. Just then the Captain appeared, attracted by the commotion. I told him that I was ordering the cadet down to solve the problem but he immediately stopped this on the grounds that the cadet might get bitten. I did think that with this particular cadet that was not too bad a thought, but it was more likely that he would bite the snake. However, the Captain had a better idea. He ordered me to contact the agent and request a snake charmer. At first I thought he was joking but he was not and, after some time, a turbanned gentleman appeared with his flute. By now the entire ship's company had joined the workers, the Chief Engineer had arrived with his sunshade, the stewards were serving drinks and the deck had taken on a party atmosphere. Everyone applauded the charmer as he entered the hold with his basket and, after a while, weird flute noises emanated from the depths. For some time there was nothing, then the charmer emerged from the hold and very seriously emptied the basket out on the deck, which caused everyone to scatter. There was no need. It was a plastic toy snake from one of the Hong Kong cargo cases that had broken open.

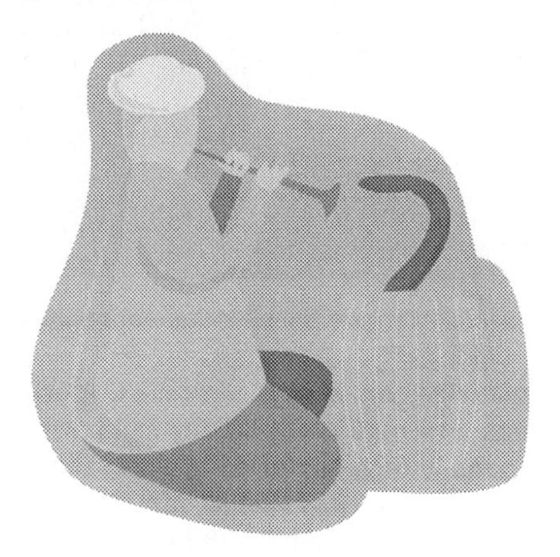

12.7 Preparing for Command

As Chief Officer, apart from performing an essential function on the ship, most of you want to become Captain. Not paper ones, real ones. So as well as learning your job as Chief Officer, you must also think about preparing yourself for command. Many Mates either have never had the opportunity or couldn't be bothered to do this and then, one day, they are in command and fervently wished they had taken the opportunity to learn more when they had the chance.

On many ships when the manoeuvring of the ship is done for port arrival and departure, the Chief Officer is stationed on the foc'sle with a junior officer on the bridge. This really doesn't make sense. A new Chief Officer coming from a background of this system has no more knowledge of the foc'sle than any other deck officer onboard, so why not put a junior officer there?

On port approaches and departures it is more important to have the experience on the bridge and that means this is where the Chief Officer should be. In addition, how is the Chief Officer going to get any experience in ship handling and close water navigation when he's stuck with the anchors?

If you find that on your ship you are expected to go forward for stations, try discussing this with the Captain and make the point that you would be more use on the bridge than forward.

If you can establish your station as the bridge rather than forward, you will be able to advance to the next stage of anchoring the ship and departing from the anchorage under the Master's supervision. As trust grows you will hopefully be able to do more of the ship handling. It is very strange that while first officers of aircraft can land and take off their aircraft, rarely are Chief Officers entrusted with the ship handling.

There are many more areas of command that you know little about, yet you would benefit greatly at this stage in your career by being shown the practical side of the job. Portage accounts are also something that the Master can show you and discuss the ways in which they are done. If the Master is willing, then take every advantage to understudy for your future.

12.8 Conflict

Be prepared.

As you already know, all Captains are not the same; they vary as much as Chief Officers do. It would be pleasant to think that on joining your ship you would find an intelligent, friendly Captain, confident in leadership and command, who would assist you when required, support you when necessary, encourage your development and allow you the freedom to run your department. Unfortunately, while there are many who are like this there are also those who are not, running the range of the disinterested to the downright unpleasant. Whatever the situation you find yourself in, it is your job to get on with the Captain, to carry out his wishes as far as you can and to support him in his position, at least for as long as you can.

In some cases, I admit that this is a tall order and there occasionally comes the time when enough is enough. The worst possible scenario is open conflict between you and the Captain and, should you experience that, the situation is nearing the time when you should request a transfer or to be relieved, with a letter to the company through the Master explaining the situation.

Not in the International code of signals.

Sometimes the mere writing of such a letter can bring a Captain to realise the circumstances and sit down with you to try to sort out the problem. It is possible that this may allow the situation to be resolved or at least improved for long enough to complete your contract.

In any real conflict between you and the Captain, while everyone and the ship will suffer, you will suffer most. First, by your opposition to him you will isolate yourself onboard. Second, you cannot win. The company will support him because, right or wrong, they have to at the time, whatever they may do later. If the conflict is allowed to continue you will be dismissed from the ship and most probably from the company. There are no industrial tribunals in international shipping and your name will be very quickly forgotten by those onboard. Whatever you do, do not try to involve others in your problem as this could escalate the situation into a very serious matter. Your alternative is to request transfer or early relief. Should you be dealing with a personnel department that insists that you continue your contract, you may be left with resigning and paying your own way home as your only alternative. That could still be preferable to staying on a ship and becoming more miserable.

Welcome relief on a long journey home?

13 Stowaways

It's not just cruise ships that carry 'guests'.

So, despite the searches undertaken in the port, a stowaway has been found, or more likely emerged from the depths of the ship or wherever he was hiding. You will now be having an interesting conversation with the Captain. He, of course, will take the final blame, but it was your search, your decks and your crew, so do not expect a cordial meeting.

However, after this you have the problem of dealing with the stowaway until he can be offloaded. The old tradition of settling him in the galley with twenty sacks of potatoes and a peeler has gone. The ship does not have the authority to force him to work, although he may volunteer. Meanwhile, you must ensure that there is no manhandling of him and that he is provided with bedding, food and, if necessary, clothing. In other words, he has to be treated like the rest of the crew while he is onboard.

It is my experience that the crew do treat them with some sympathy and generally extend a gruff kindness. You will be guided by the Master as to their condition onboard but remember that, while they are on the ship, their welfare and security are your responsibility. If you arrive in port and they are not being repatriated there are very strict fines if they disappear. Under these circumstances they can be put under lock and key in the ship, but if you feel that you cannot deal with or guarantee such security then you must advise the Master. Hopefully he will then make arrangements for shore security to ensure the compliance with the port's administration.

14 Piracy

Just a brief mention of this problem as the incident figures, which are published each year, continue to grow. The security precautions at sea will be declared in your SMS guide and the Master will state his requirements when transiting certain areas.

If you are on smaller ships regularly trading in high risk areas, it is wise not to keep too much of your cash onboard and to take out personal effects insurance as it is unlikely that your company will reimburse you for your losses.

Both in port and at sea, your ship is not the place for heroics. The chances are that the pirates will be armed and you are not, so that really indicates that the path to take is acceptance of the inevitable. Give them what they want and, hopefully, off they will go. Understandably, this is not the way we would like to deal with the situation but, without weapons, there is probably very little you can do unless it is just a casual robbery by one or two persons. In trying to take any action, you must also consider the others onboard who may suffer as a result of your conduct.

One of the definitions of piracy is an act of robbery on the seas. This has lead to any act of theft while the ship is under way or at anchor being an act of piracy. One man boarding and stealing a paint can while the ship is at anchor is hardly an act of piracy yet, because of the definition, it is included in the overall figures. Real piracy, with the perpetrators armed and ready to commit acts of violence to gain their aims, is extremely serious and all must be done to reduce danger to those onboard.

Simple theft can be reduced by good lookouts at anchorages or by not anchoring in high risk areas. When at anchor you should ensure that all storerooms are locked and high risk equipment is stowed away in a secure place. Access from the decks should be limited to a single door. Good deck lighting, with additional lights placed over the side and the duty watch taking an occasional turn around the decks, provide the signs of an alert ship and will assist in deterring the casual thief.

15 Passengers

High expectations?

For many Chief Officers, these are an evil necessity. I am not talking about cruise ships where passengers are the lifeblood, but the smaller numbers that tend to venture onto cargo ships. For the Captain and others onboard they provide, with a few reservations, a pleasant addition to the ship. The food usually improves as well. However, passengers mean that their cabins require looking after. A passenger with a blocked lavatory/W.C. is not so willing to wait till morning to get it fixed, even if they did block it in the first place. Doors loose on hinges that rattle or something rolling in the deckhead are the kind of work that, if just dealing with the ship's company, you could give them a screwdriver and say 'fix it yourself', but not so with a passenger. While there may be extra catering staff onboard, there is no addition to the deck crew.

They will want to go on deck, which is very inconsiderate but you can't lock them in their cabins! That means clean washed down decks every day, deckchairs washed, put out in the morning and taken in at night and of course the swimming pool, if you have one, has to be cleaned out each day, not filled with junk as happens on so many ships. Add that to the fact that, unlike cruise ships where you can stuff passengers full of food and drink, take their money and pour them back down the gangway after a couple of weeks, these passengers tend to remain for months and, inevitably feel that they know the ship better than you and are happy to point out to the Captain various faults with your department and possibly yourself.

So the Chief Officer has a point when he feels that passengers are not necessarily a happy event onboard. Either way, you must ensure that the various requirements that fall on your department are undertaken to ensure their welfare and pleasure are catered for. They have paid for their passage and, in the end, you should want to ensure that they have a pleasant voyage in the ship. Your constant courtesy is of course expected.

One particular morning, I had already had an interesting conversation with the Captain as someone had the temerity to leave an oily footprint on his otherwise immaculately holystoned deck. We had onboard an elderly rather deaf lady with her nasty little terrier named Dolly. The problem was that not only did this brute frequently make various deposits over the white wooden decks, but each time the sailors tried to clean it up or even walk by the thing changed into a crocodile and bit them. After some days spent having the messes cleaned up and the sailors patched up, this particular morning was the limit, with two heaps of dung and the Bosun bitten. I suggested to the lady that we should make a kennel to keep Dolly from falling over the side. From the Bosun's remarks, this was a distinct possibility. That evening, all the passengers were looking at me in horror and, when summoned to the Captain's cabin after dinner, it transpired that the lady had told all that I had threatened to nail Dolly in a box and throw her over the side. No matter the distortion of truth, I had to apologise to the lady and to Dolly, and vow life membership of the RSPCA to all the other passengers. The only good thing that came out of it was that the Bosun and the crew thought I was a great chap and they wanted to make the box.

16 The Workforce

For the first time, you will be directly in charge of crew and responsible for their work and wellbeing. This is a serious responsibility, particularly on a ship where they cannot go home at the end of the day and relax from the pressures of work. One of the problems of living on the job is the inability to escape from it. Another problem is the ease with which you can be called out at any time for further work, although you have done many hours already. I always remember as a cadet being told in port that if you are onboard you are working. We used to go ashore purely to escape this directive, particularly when we were on ships where overtime was paid so it was always the cadets who were called out before the crew.

16.1 The ILO Convention on Hours of Work

ILO Convention No.180 requires:

> *Every seafarer must be provided with not less than 10 hours rest in total in any 24 hour period, provided that:*
>
> *The 10 hour period may be divided into not more than two periods one of which shall be not less than 6 hours; and*
>
> *The interval between consecutive periods of rest shall not exceed 14 hours; and*
>
> *The minimum hours of rest shall not be less than 77 hours in any 7 day period.*

Sounds as if you have unlimited crew to call upon! As we all know, your deck crew could range from only two and upwards, depending on the type of ship you are on. There will never be enough, which is why it is essential to plan their work so that no time is wasted.

On 25th November 1999, the IMO adopted Resolution A.890(21), Principles of Safe Manning. It stated:

> *The minimum safe manning level of a ship should be established taking into account all relevant factors, including the following:*
>
> 1) *Size and type of ship;*
> 2) *number, size and type of main propulsion units and auxiliaries;*
> 3) *construction and equipment of the ship;*
> 4) *method of maintenance used;*
> 5) *cargo to be carried;*
> 6) *frequency of port calls, length and nature of voyages to be undertaken;*
> 7) *trading area(s), waters and operations in which the ship is involved;*
> 8) *extent to which training activities are conducted onboard; and*
> 9) *applicable work hour limits and/or rest requirements.*

The above is sensible and, if followed, should provide a sound basis from which to ascertain the manning level. The Resolution goes on to list the functions on which the safe minimum manning levels should be based and include:

> *Moor and unmoor the ship safely.*
>
> *Maintain a safe navigational watch in accordance with the requirements of the STCW Code.*

Finally, and most important:

> *The number of qualified and other personnel required to meet* ***peak workload situations and conditions****, with due regard to the number of hours of shipboard duties and rest periods assigned to seafarers.*

The majority of shipping companies, coastguards and other authorities concerned with manning, regrettably seem to have missed the word '*peak*'.

16.2 Working Hours

Never enough, but there never have been enough on any ship for a demanding Chief Officer. In present day circumstances every hour is valuable, which is why work planning is more important than ever before. Let us take an example of a 160,000 dwt bulk carrier with a Bosun and 5 seamen. With a working day of

8 hours and 4 hours on Saturdays, you will, theoretically, get 44 hours a week of work out of each man, but we know that this is not possible. From the workforce must be deducted 3 men who, at sea, are watchkeeping on the bridge. We will look at this requirement more closely later but, suffice to say, your workforce is severely affected. Now into the mix put your smokos of an hour a day, deduct an hour a week for drills and you can see your available work time fast disappearing.

In port the situation is even worse, particularly with security taking up 3 men for gangway duties. By the time cargo and storing duties have encroached on your workforce there is little left. An example is, how does a bulk carrier clean off the hatch trackways, close and secure 9 hatches, and prepare the ship for sea with only 3 men? The answer is it cannot, so the security on the gangway is abandoned right at the time it is needed most and the ship is often put to sea in an unprepared state.

The working hours and times are not inflexible and, with a good crew, you might often find that flexibility can be used to improve the work and life in the ship. If the ship is heading to a 'good port', of which there are a few left, then the chances are that most crew would like a run ashore. In that case you will find that quite often they would prefer to work longer hours at sea before arrival and have time off in port. Or, on arrival at the port, you could introduce 'job and finish', which again gets you your work done and allows the crew a break when the work is completed.

In the tropics you will very quickly note that, while the crew work well in the morning, in the afternoon they slow down noticeably, particularly if you are not around. Consider changing the hours to 0600 to 1400. This has worked to everyone's advantage on many ships.

Seamen are a traditional bunch, so before making any changes in their routine consult with them and explain the reasons why. Add in the proviso that if it does not work then you are willing to change back to the normal routine. At least that way they will be more willing to give it a try.

16.3 Overtime

Is overtime now a last resort?

This method of payment seems to be dying out fast but there are ships and companies where it is still paid. It is a mixed blessing. Your ability to get work done is now limited not by your working day but by the company, which imposes limits on the overtime that can be paid. It is also subject to abuse by the Bosun awarding hours to those in favour and keeping it from those who are not.

The good side is that it can be used as an unofficial disciplinary tool and it can ensure that you can get work completed beyond the working day.

Be careful if you have cadets onboard that you do not use them as a cheaper labour force. It is very tempting for Chief Officers to call out the cadets instead of the crew when overtime is required to be paid.

16.4 Planning the Work

During the course of your available work times, you will be in three differing work environments:

- Sea - good weather
- sea - bad weather
- in port.

Each of these presents a hindrance and an opportunity.

You know what work is required to be done, both inside the ship and outside. Considering the general vagaries of weather, unless you are cruising along in the South Pacific, you have to be ready for both types. This means that, together with your Bosun, you will keep two jobs ongoing, one outside and one inside. The men can instantly change from one to the other without the delays involved in finding something for them to do when the weather changes.

From this it follows that you will have three lists of work, outside, inside and port. If you can see ahead to make up a work book with these separate lists, why not put alongside each job the tools required and the risk assessment number applicable to that job. This can then be given to the Bosun, who will ensure that the appropriate tools are ready for use and that the risk assessment is brought to the attention of those doing the job. It really is a simple way of ensuring that the work is done more efficiently and that the SMS is followed.

Finally, remember that your officers are not there for manual labour nor do you have the authority to order them to do the same. The fact that they occasionally will give a hand at a task must be regarded as a bonus. Also your cadets are not there as part of your workforce. They are onboard for training and again, while they can be given tasks to do that are relevant to the ship and are extremely helpful in supplementing your available crew, they must not be regarded permanently in this role.

16.5 Safety at Work

Of course safety must have prime consideration, but how much time do you allot to this? If you read your company's SMS manuals you can never do enough, but you have the rest of the ship to care for as well.

Therefore, although I will put safety at the head of the work schedule, if this is not something that is taken care of in the normal planned maintenance programme it must have priority. Remember that the work is intended to make the equipment safe and usable, not necessarily to make it look good.

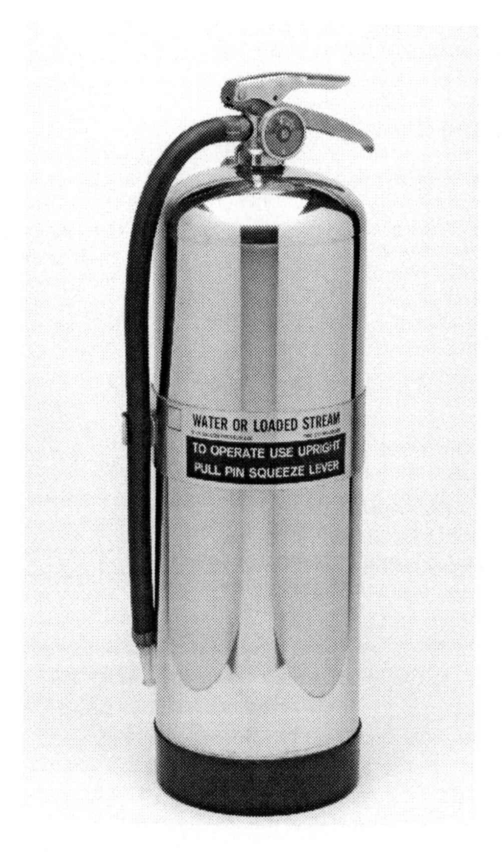

Just because it looks good does not mean it works.

I once had a fire in the accommodation and, when it was put out, the crew member who tackled the fire was asked why he did not use the accommodation fire extinguisher outside the cabin. He said that as it was polished he thought that it was not to be used!

16.6 Planned Maintenance

The planned maintenance schedules of your ship may be excellent and well thought out, having been made up by ex-sea staff in consultation with existing sea staff. On the other hand, they could have been made up by some technical department member of staff who may have never been to sea or, in the worst cases, been based on those of another company.

Keeping abreast of the planned maintenance will take a large proportion of your available workforce. Your daily work schedule will revolve around this and safety will be built into it. By all means plan around this but do not necessarily be governed by it. It is advisable to look ahead and see what is going to be required over the next few days. Look at the ship's schedule and the weather forecast. This should enable you to list the work that is essential to be completed. Then list the work that can be done in good weather and bad weather.

You are hopefully experienced enough to know that on a modern ship a tick (✓) by something is not always a guarantee that a particular task has been done. It also means 'can't be bothered' or 'I am far too busy to check all this'. In some cases, what is required and the frequency it is required to be done by is incorrect and you can allow leeway on these items, but you must ensure that this interpretation of the schedule is with your knowledge and discussed with the Bosun. By doing this, you establish that it is not a general free for all. There are other times when you simply will not have the men or time to complete all the required tasks. If that is the case, then you should make a separate note and ensure that they are completed as soon as possible.

This is the reason why you make your frequent inspection tours of your decks. If important maintenance should have been done but has not, this is the only way to find out. If this has occurred without your knowledge, come down hard on it otherwise it will carry on. If maintenance is required by the schedule, but from inspection it is not required and not a priority, then you can leave it for more important work.

16.7 Cross Departmental Maintenance

This is tricky and can be the cause of dispute if not handled correctly. There are many items of maintenance to be done by other departments, notably the engineering department, in areas within your responsibility - hydraulic leaks, lighting, winches and windlasses to name just a few. Areas such as the galley, accommodation and rescue boat also require combined departmental effort. With good officers, the willingness is there and the desire to do things correctly but, just the same as in your department, the other departments are under the same pressure of too few people and time and there are occasions when other more pressing concerns override the maintenance requirements. Always discuss concerns you have with the Second Engineer. He will undoubtedly explain why something cannot be done immediately but will have been reminded that an item needs attention, and so will get to it when he can.

On the other hand, if items are neglected and, after such reminders, are still not being attended to and there is no good reason, then you must speak with the department head, in most cases the Chief Engineer. If there is no cooperation received from this quarter then you must go the Captain. This might not make you the most popular officer onboard but you have placed your department ahead of personal comfort and carried out your job correctly. Certainly you must ensure that items under dispute do not get signed for as complete, which again is not easy, particularly if the Chief Engineer is in charge of maintenance.

You will plan your work schedule with the Bosun. The days when the Bosun was a man promoted after many years at sea with all the knowledge and experience that brings are long gone, unless you are very lucky. Hopefully though, he will have several years in his job and will be able to join with you in the work plan.

By this I mean the tasks on a ship that are often a point of dispute as to who looks after them. Many of these have been caused by the removal of those who traditionally looked after them. As an example who should clean out the deck lights, the deck or engine department?

It is wise to see where these tasks exist and sit down with the other senior officers and try to determine as to which department deals with these. Otherwise it could be that with no one responsible the jobs don't get done until something goes wrong.

There should also be flexibility. On a modern ship just because one department has responsibility for a certain task, does not mean that another department cannot lend a helping hand and take on the task if the responsible department has more urgent matters to attend to.

16.8 PPE

We all understand that PPE has to be worn when engaged in areas of risk in the workplace, but you have to be reasonable about this. If you can be sensible about where you want PPE worn then you have a better chance of seeing that your instructions are carried out. The problem is that should any freak accident occur, such as someone falling over the side, the fact that he wasn't wearing a hard hat will become the main issue. You will have to live with this for your crew will not be keen on wearing hard hats out on deck while painting in 40°C, but they will when going into the deep tanks for inspection. It is all a matter of sensible enforcement.

In wearing this equipment, you and the other officers must set the example. If you are wearing it then the crew are obliged to follow your example, but if you are not, then an attitude of complacency will set in.

16.9 PPE Maintenance

If you have the equipment it has to be effective. Crew are not going to wear goggles if the plastiglass is scratched and dulled. Nor will they wear them if they are uncomfortable. Gloves are not much good if they are worn through, or the work clothing if it is ragged or torn, or the shoes if they don't fit.

When you join and get out to sea, have a check of all your department's PPE and work clothing. If there is equipment that needs replacing, get this done and ensure that the clothing is in good order. I accept that this might be easier said than done. There are companies who believe that crew can survive with 2 boiler suits a year or should provide their own and do not issue any. This is a problem. All you can do if the required items are not onboard is make a request through the Master for an emergency storing order on the grounds of safety. If the situation is serious, you do not have any usable goggles for example, then you cannot do any work requiring these until the appropriate equipment is supplied. Advise the Master of this as well and that might stir some action. Also remember that some items of PPE, such as helmets, have an expiry date.

16.10 Working with the Crew

There are those who, for some reason, think that by working with the crew they are showing an example of leadership. Either that or they are trying to impress all onboard with their industry and dedication. I once relieved a Chief Officer who met me in a boiler suit with a chipping hammer in his hand and spent the handover time telling me all that he had done and that I had time to finish off painting the port davits before sailing. Unfortunately, all the other aspects of his work were a disaster area and the crew thought that he was a joke. In other words, he was using the simple task of chipping on deck to avoid tackling his proper responsibilities.

You are not the Bosun and the crew do not like you working with them. You are a senior officer of the ship and should behave like one.

17 Training

Experience is training and all onboard are engaged in some form it, even the Captain. This is because, regardless of what you know, every ship is different in construction, equipment or even in the attitude it presents to the seas. So each day is a new experience in which nothing is certain or to be taken for granted.

Trainees, like their background and education are all different.

The basic seamanship of trainees onboard, whether they are officer cadets or ratings, will vary depending on the country that they come from. Hopefully you will have more than one cadet because training just one is far more difficult than two. Two cadets can work together, bounce ideas off each other and generally keep each other company, and therefore out from under your feet. Also the problem if there is one cadet is that he tends to become the Chief Officer's runner. It is normal for cadets to have a training schedule with a training record book, which in theory ensures that cadets have completed training in a certain subject before moving on to the next. Regrettably, this is often a 'tick the right box' situation, with not enough time to ensure that the cadet has really understood and completed the subject matter. But for his training to be completed the box has to be ticked, so it is.

As soon as you can, get the cadets' training record books and just ask a few questions based on what they are supposed to know and you will soon have a good idea as to what has been going on. If the rating trainees do not have a training book then make one up for them, so that both you and they have a record of what they have done.

The days of giving cadets the most dangerous jobs onboard, on the basis that they were the cheapest and easiest to replace by opening another box, are long gone. No more selling them in Casablanca either!

On a very busy ship, with low manning, it is very tempting to use cadets as cheap labour. But you shouldn't. You must also be careful before you put them into hazardous situations. As an example, should they drive the windlass on the foc'sle? If you are on a 160,000 dwt vessel and have only 5 seafarers to moor the ship it is very tempting, but it must be a question of experience. If they are new to the job, whether rating or cadet, then they cannot be allowed near any such hazard, particularly in poor weather with heavy strains on the lines.

If you have a number of trainees onboard, make the Third Officer the training officer. It will help give him confidence in dealing with the crew and, as he is a Third Officer, his own knowledge will be fresh to pass on and he can relate well to the trainees. However, having put him in this position, you should have a weekly check on both his and the trainees' progress.

With regard to the cadets, remember that they will only have one year's initial sea time and, of that, 6 months are supposed to be for seamanship. You must do what you can to imbue the cadet with the basics and what you consider important. On joining a ship they should first go on the deck. If there is only one cadet he should be put with the Bosun, ensuring that the Bosun has a list of the priorities.

If there are two cadets, they can be tasked together by the Bosun or worked with the crew. Either way, they must start with the dirtiest hardest work on the ship. This brings them down to earth and provides them with a taste of what it takes to keep the ship going.

17.1 Rules of the Road

Rules of the road or if, you prefer, collision avoidance, is still the basic requirement for any watchkeeping officer and part of the training for all deck cadets should be continuous instruction in the rules. Sunday morning doing mock orals with either yourself or the Captain can be invaluable instruction for the cadet, not only to learn the rules but also to prepare for his forthcoming examinations.

18 Fatigue

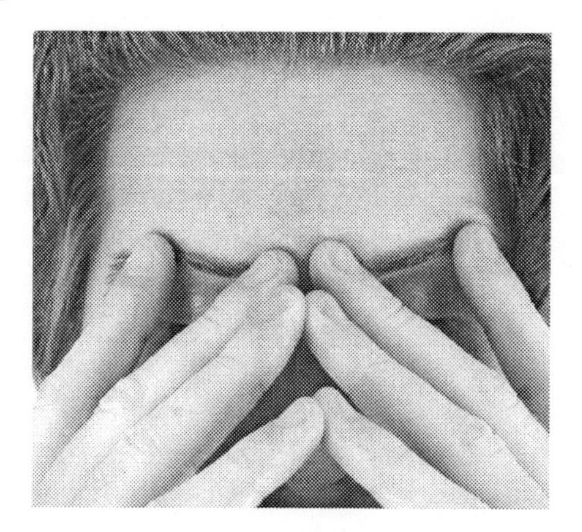

The two most important factors affecting safety are manning and fatigue.

18.1 The Effects of Fatigue

> *From MSC/Circ 1014: Alertness is the optimum state of the brain that enables us to make conscious decisions. Fatigue has a proven detrimental effect on alertness – this can be readily seen when a person is required to maintain a period of concentrated and sustained attention, such as looking out for the unexpected (eg night watch).*

When a person's alertness is affected by fatigue, their performance on the job can be significantly impaired. Impairment will occur in every aspect of human performance (physically, emotionally and mentally) such as in decision-making, response time, judgement, hand-eye coordination and countless other skills.

Fatigued individuals become more susceptible to errors of attention and memory (for example, it is not uncommon for fatigued individuals to omit steps in a sequence).

Chronically fatigued individuals will often select strategies that have a high degree of risk on the basis that they require less effort to execute.

Fatigue can affect an individual's ability to respond to stimuli, perceive stimuli and interpret or understand stimuli, and it can take longer to react to them once they have been identified.

Fatigue also affects problem solving, which is an integral part of handling new or novel tasks.

Fatigue is known to detrimentally affect a person's performance and may reduce individual and crew effectiveness and efficiency, decrease productivity, lower standards of work and even lead to errors being made. Unless steps are taken to alleviate the fatigue, it will pose a hazard to ship safety.

18.2 Safe Working Ethics

Many of the jobs that will be done on the ship are unsafe. Simply being at sea on some ships can be called that. If we accept this then, no matter what we do, we cannot make many of these tasks completely safe. However, we can ensure that equipment and tools are correct and safe and that the correct PPE is worn.

The next question is whether or not those about to use the equipment actually know how to use it? This might seem a little strange but, as an example, can the trainee rig the Bosun's chair properly? It is a bit late finding out when it is slipping twenty metres above the deck.

The weather must also be considered. If you are taking seas and rolling or pitching heavily, you must consider whether, the work is so essential that it must be done and the risk accepted.

Risk Assessment, when used sensibly, can be of benefit. If you find that you disagree with the assessment of any item or practice, you must advise the safety officer and make a reassessment. If this reassessment involves any work that could endanger life, before it is distributed you should advise the Master of the proposed changes and the reasons why. Properly used, the assessment should only take a few minutes before commencing any job, but it is important that the crew and you are reminded of the important factors of the intended task.

In the event of any accident the shore investigators will review your assessment, so be careful. It is better to follow the rules than to risk life and your career to save few minutes of time, regardless of how hard you are pressed. Of course there are urgent circumstances when action must be taken immediately and there is no time for such assessment. At sea, we all know that but, unfortunately, it is difficult to simulate the urgency of the moment in the quiet hush of the office ashore or a courtroom.

Before your mind turns to shortcuts, remember that the courts can be very sobering.

19 Leadership and Attitude

You may have had pre-sea training on a traditional training ship or shore establishment that gave you some leadership training and an understanding of it. However, it is more likely that you will not have had this advantage and, during your time as Third and Second Officer, you might have had little to do with leading the crew except for at stations in and out of ports.

A lot of leadership is about having confidence in yourself. You don't have to know every answer to every situation, just have confidence to ask others their advice and use that with your own knowledge and abilities to produce a feasible resolution. Most, if not all, of your crew onboard want to be led, which makes it easier. I understand the difficulties perceived by younger officers dealing with older people, and different nationalities when dealing with each other. There exists a certain embarrassment, possibly a feeling that it should be the other way around. If this exists, it is likely to be in your mind, not theirs. If your orders are sensible and properly given in a pleasant manner, then you will find that those receiving them have no difficulty in carrying them out. Resentment comes not from age, race or nationality, but from being given orders in an unpleasant way or that are stupid.

Your general attitude while on the ship is, therefore, most important. On every ship there are those who seem to make a hobby of complaining regardless of their circumstances. It is essential that this is not you. Obviously, you cannot be cheerful all the time, and if you go around with a perpetual grin on your face the crew will consider you a clown that doesn't know what is going on. But if you can be generally cheerful with a ready word and smile for those onboard, you set an example to others. Carry this further and be ready with a word of praise for those who do their work properly, rather than taking them for granted. Not only will you find that this helps the ship, particularly when in difficult circumstances, but the respect for you will grow, and rightly so.

Finally, never shout at or argue with your men.

19.1 Delegation

You will know, and probably are quite tired of being told, of all the differing tasks and responsibilities associated with the ship that used to be carried out by the junior officers and cadets. Chief Engineers could leave the engine room for days before going down for a walk around. Captains and Chief Officers could go ashore without too many concerns about the ship. The watch on the bridge would rarely have to be checked on, even in the busiest of traffic. The Master only went on the bridge to keep a watchful eye on the situation in case an officer needed his advice. So what has happened? We still have the Second and Third Officers and we are told by countless administrations and ship operators that their quality is still the same. If that is the case, then why are the company, the Master and even you not willing to delegate to these officers the responsibilities they once held, making them accountable for their actions?

A number of companies now try to insist that either the Master or the Chief Officer must be onboard the ship at all times. This is a gross interference with the ship and the Master's authority. We are content to let an officer have charge of the bridge for eight hours a day yet when in port, where the ship is far safer, he cannot be entrusted to run the ship? Is a company that makes such rules stating that not only do they not trust their Second or Third Officers, but that they do not trust the Master or Chief Officer to make a reasoned judgement as to when they can leave the vessel? Surely if the officers are not capable of assuming such responsibilities they should not be on the ship in the first place?

However, in many cases it is us who are unwilling to delegate responsibility. While this is understandable, it does neither you nor the officer any favours. If you do not delegate duties and accountability to an officer, how will they to learn to grow into position.

19.2 Morale

The morale on a ship depends on many factors, some of which you have no control over. However, the morale onboard or, if you prefer, the level of contentment or happiness, does affect the work, safety and efficiency of the ship. Because we cannot quantify this in a financial way, it can often be hard to convince operators of the need for their interest in the maintenance of morale.

While you cannot have control over the ports of call, the availability of shore leave, the weather, the equipment onboard or, often regrettably, the personality of the

Captain, there are things that you can do that will assist in either maintaining good morale or raising it. As the Chief Officer of the ship you must consider this as part of your function.

We discussed entertainment, such as the provision of DVDs, books, etc, as being part of your job, but you should also be able to order stores items such as dartboards, gym equipment and similar.

The quality of the food and cooking will have a very large bearing on the morale of the crew and if there is any discontentment regarding this you should bring it to the attention of the Captain.

20 Accommodation and Catering

On a small ship, the 'department' could well be just the Cook. In this situation, the deck department will take over the accommodation cleaning and often will peel the potatoes at night! The small size of the crew will allow far more flexibility with the storing and it is common on these ships for a monthly allowance to be paid for the ship, that the cook can spend where and when he pleases. This generally ensures, provided the ship is making frequent port calls, that the food is fresh and of better quality than that supplied by chandlers. If the order is big enough, supermarkets will often deliver to the ship.

On small ships a trip to the supermarket may be better.

On larger vessels the department has to be more formally organised, with work schedules and management. Too often this now devolves on the Cook, simply by the company changing his title to Cook/Chief Steward as if a title is going to make him into a Chief Steward. The Cook will often be a good cook, but will not necessarily understand the running of a department, so you could find this becomes your responsibility. You may find there are no work schedules and that considerable time is wasted, which is something you must deal with carefully and with a light hand.

20.1 The Accommodation

The accommodation is the area most likely to be neglected by the company and the technical department superintendents, with some accommodation and fittings unchanged until the ship is scrapped, sometimes some 30 years later.

Your department is responsible for the fabric of the accommodation and this includes the carpentry, plumbing and electrical fittings. Common sense dictates that there will be limitations to what you are capable of doing

You will notice very quickly that, when there is a problem with the engineering or navigational aspect of the ship that is beyond the capacity of the ship's staff to deal with, shore labour is called in to assist. However, if you call for shore labour for a problem with the accommodation it is a totally different story, even though you do not have the expertise to change locks, repair doors or even anything beyond the basic rudiments of plumbing and carpentry.

I once joined a ship where all the lavatories/W.C.s had been locked except one. The company's technical department would not allow shore labour for accommodation repairs and so, as things went wrong, they were simply shut down. When I spoke to senior management about the problem they were very upset at such a situation and immediately authorised the necessary repairs.

Everyone onboard is entitled to well maintained clean accommodation. Power points must work, cabin doors must lock and keys must be available. Curtains must not be rags and carpeting must be clean. In other words, regardless of the company, think 'hotel standard', and work towards this.

20.2 Cleanliness

The accommodation will be your home for some months, but for the crew it might be home for a year or more. The cleanliness of the accommodation is not only important for those living in it, but also for the appearance and presentation of the ship to the visitors that come onboard in various ports.

If you are in charge of the catering and cleanliness of the accommodation, have crew use quick dry instant shine polish then indent for kraft paper and seal this down with tape over the decks before arrival in every port. In this way you preserve the condition of your decks from unthinking visitors with dirty shoes. Another tip is to purchase plug-in air fresheners as they are far more effective than sprays. Try to keep visitors away from the living quarters as much as possible. Where this is unavoidable, put notices up reminding shore personnel that this is your home. Ample door mats are essential and not the cheap bristle kind that sheds the bristles to block scuppers! Make sure they are rubber backed to avoid slipping. For some odd reason, many modern ships have scuppers in the accommodation many decks up, maybe the naval architects' 'how to build a ship' books have yet to be updated! Of course, what happens is that no one puts water down them and they smell. To prevent this I suggest sealing them up, unless you want to implement a strict regime of pouring disinfectant down them every week.

It is not always the shore people who dirty the accommodation and you might have to educate the ship's personnel as well. One of the perennial problems on a ship is that of officers and crew keeping their dirty boilersuits in their cabins. Most ships have lockers for working clothing to be stored in and I advise that you insist they are used. Oily boilersuits not only cause dirt on the cabin bulkheads but also cause bad smell through the accommodation, so there is justification that they should not be kept in cabins.

A weekly essential.

Ensure that the weekly issue of soap and towels is rigidly kept to and that the bed linen is changed at the same time. If there is steward service in the officers' cabins ensure that this is completed properly. Having said that, it is not easy for a steward to clean a cabin if the occupant is dirty and untidy in his habits. There could well be times when the steward is perfectly justified in not coping with a particular cabin.

20.3 Bedding

This is possibly the most neglected area on merchant ships today. Thousands of ships are sailing around with mattresses 20 years old or more. Stained and torn sheets are often the norm and laundry discipline non-existent. While SOLAS deals with all other aspects of safety, and Port State Control and Coastguard officials visit and inspect the ship, no one bothers with the accommodation.

If you find a poor situation, you must immediately indent for new mattresses and bedding linen. If the Master does not do this, you must ensure that a strict inspection regime is in place and that the crew regularly wash their bedding. Watch out at inspection times for a counterpane being pulled over dirty bedding.

New mattress?

I once joined a ship that we were taking back from a company after a long bareboat charter. The mattresses were teeming with lice and had not been changed since the ship was built 15 years before. The port where we were situated had to send down a special fumigation team to take them ashore and burn them.

20.4 The Messrooms

The crew messroom tends to be used as the general lounge area as well as for meals, even if the crew have a separate lounge. There is nothing wrong with this, particularly if the lounge area is clean, as crew wearing their working clothes throughout the day are not going to change to sit down for a cup of tea. If the catering department does not clean this area, the Bosun should determine who does. Owing to the different departments using the messrooms and other crew public areas, it is usually a fairer system to establish a rota so that each crew member and department shares the responsibility.

The crew public rooms are for crew use and are not a canteen for the shore labour, who will gravitate towards these areas if they can get away with it. Keep all shore personnel out of the accommodation unless they have an official reason to be there. Prior to arrival, post notices on all the entrance doors stating that only ship's crew are allowed in the accommodation area without official permission. This will at least cut down the traffic.

20.5 The Galley

A place to be wary of as it is the lair of the Cook who is, for all intents and purposes, the most important person on the ship, and knows it.

The galley is the one place where cleanliness and hygiene have to prevail. Most cooks do realise this and each evening have the galley washed down. It is an area that requires your attention, even if just to pass through, letting all know it is being watched. Clean clothing is essential as is hand washing and towels, preferably paper towels from a dispenser. Once again, you may have to indent for aprons, trousers, shoes and hats.

20.6 Infestation

I have only been on one ship without cockroaches and that was a ship that had never been east of Gibraltar. Almost every ship, including tramps, bulkers, tankers, container ships or cruise ships, has cockroaches. Once they have established themselves the only way to remove them is to do a complete fumigation of the accommodation which, because of the need to remove the crew and all stores, is something very few owners will consider.

Sometimes just keeping control will be all that can be achieved.

You can generally get local fumigation onboard, if you push hard enough, and this might just keep them under control if done regularly and properly.

Doing this, while maintaining excellent hygiene in the galley, messrooms and food stores, leaving no food out there or in the cabins and carrying out standard onboard spraying, should keep them within acceptable limits. As they inhabit spaces behind the bulkheads, particularly in the galley, you will need to have holes drilled in the bulkheads at regular intervals to get the chemicals inside. Ensure that you have a proper spray system as the cans of spray are only effective for cabin use.

21 Safety

Remember why you are doing the job.

A ship is an inherently dangerous vehicle travelling on a potentially hazardous medium presenting a very real danger to the incautious. There are many deaths and injuries every year and, while some of these are genuine accidents that could not have been prevented by any rules or regulations, the vast majority are preventable by recognising the dangers and taking the appropriate precautions.

You will have been lectured so much on safety, with repetitive books, posters and DVDs littering the ships that you, in common with many others, are heartily sick of the word. But if we have had so much stuffed into our heads about it, why is it that we continue to have men swept off foc'sles, dying in tanks, killed by moorings and crushed on the decks, with the subsequent wreckage of lives, families and careers?

There are a few simple ground rules:

- We are not at war, we are engaged in commerce. No company, ship or task is worth injury or dying for
- any order that puts a man in danger is illegal
- all of us have more responsibility to our family than to the ship
- if anyone wishes to put their life or limbs in danger, then that is their decision not yours
- those working under your authority are your responsibility
- just think.

21.1 ISM

When we say 'officer in charge of ISM', we tend to mean the officer who files all the amendments, often without reading them, and who goes around the ship at the end of the month ensuring that everyone signs the monthly bits of paper, particularly the hours of work. If you have a vast safety department in the office, they do tend to forget that the ship is limited in its clerical abilities and that the more that is churned out the less is read. The modern ship desperately needs a ship's clerk but you are highly unlikely to get one.

The paperwork can seem endless.

There is a danger that complacency and excess paperwork mean we do not keep up to date with ISM guidance, putting ourselves into danger should something go wrong.

If you accept that the ISM Guide onboard is meant to assist you rather than provide the company with a way to blame you should something go wrong, then your own attitude to it will be responsive rather than antagonistic, which unfortunately, too many officers are becoming.

21.2 The Paper Chase

Try to spread the load.

The whole of the system depends on good record keeping and its inspection. When this has to be done by only one person you can see how he may become overloaded, particularly when he is under pressure from his other duties. You should make an effort to see that the paperwork is shared out. For example, the deck officers do not have to fill in the monthly hours of work for everyone, which occurs on some ships. Hand out the blank forms to the crew and let them be responsible for filling them in. If the problem is that allowable hours might be exceeded, I suggest that it is better that the true hours are written so that something can be done about the situation, although on one ship I was in we did exactly that, only to have them returned and ordered to fill them in 'correctly'!

One form that you should personally care for is the risk assessments. They shape the safety of all the work that is done onboard and it is important that they are not only kept up to date, but that they are read and acted upon. This is the reason why they should not be stuffed into some corner of the bridge and only taken out a few weeks before audit and hastily added to, but kept in a place where all can access them, especially those doing the work.

Make one of your officers responsible for the updating of all non-navigational and ISM documentation. This is quite a job with the paper flow now coming up the gangway, but if it is just one officer he will at least know where the documents are and what has been done. The Second Officer, traditionally the navigating officer, will be busy enough with the charts and navigational updates.

This leaves you with the standard garbage records, chain registers, watch lists, station muster cards, Chief Officer's logbook and other sundry work.

At the end of the month the Master should examine the system and see that the paperwork is being completed. If this is not occurring on your ship, do it yourself.

21.3 Safety Officer

Every company seems to have differing ideas about who the safety officer should be and what his designation is, and even onboard there is some confusion about his responsibilities. In theory, once whoever is designated safety officer puts that hat on they are the only truly independent person onboard, even of the Captain. Remember, this is the theory. This officer is responsible for all the day-to-day safety matters onboard and it is his duty to bring to the attention of the appropriate officer any fault, neglect or failure in any aspect of safety. However, it is hard enough when the safety officer is a senior officer but when, as often happens, it is a junior officer, he tends to be a voice in the wilderness.

If this is the case on your ship it is a pity, as this officer can and should perform a valuable function onboard that assists you rather than hinders. If the safety officer is a junior officer, regardless of department, you should let him know that you are receptive to comments and that your support is there, and also that you expect him to advise you of any deficiency he observes. When he does this, then regardless of your feelings towards his comments, you have a duty to respond to them in a reasonable way. By this, you encourage him to do his job properly.

The safety officer's job is not just dealing with equipment or work; his responsibilities span all activities onboard, even fatigue. However, how many Captains are willing to sit down with a junior safety officer and listen while he is told that he should not have sailed his ship as the crew were fatigued? That would be an interesting conversation, which is why it is difficult for a junior officer to take on the job.

If you are the safety officer then, as your department is responsible for the maintenance of all the safety equipment, this is not as easy as it sounds. How do you criticise yourself? All of this means that the safety officer, in theory and in practice, on a ship, in close continual contact with his colleagues for many months, is not and cannot be the free agent that he is supposed to be.

How can we resolve this problem of duty, egos, personalities and rank to enable the function of the safety officer to be carried out to the benefit of the ship?

The committee 'should' be elected.

By law, every ship that has a safety committee must have members elected onboard. If any ship actually has an election this is very unusual, and I certainly have never seen one or heard of one. How the cruise ships are supposed to have elections with constantly changing large numbers of crew has yet to be debated. So let us assume that on your ship, in common with most, the safety committee consists of appointed representatives from each department.

This committee can meet informally each week and there the safety officer can raise matters of safety that he has noted, with a brief record made of the meeting and points resolved. If there are any matters that cannot be resolved at the meeting they should be noted and a written response requested from the department concerned.

In this way, the face to face meeting between junior and senior is avoided and a calmer considered reply can be written. The fact that each department can have its say should also provoke a more reasoned acceptance of such a system.

If you are not the safety officer, you must assist him or at least sympathise with his position, particularly if he is a junior officer and trying to take his position seriously. If you support all efforts and provide advice when required, this will considerably enhance his position onboard.

21.4 Safety Meetings

If the company wants these to be held weekly, it is reasonable for only the safety committee to attend. If, on the other hand, the committee only meets monthly, which is perfectly reasonable and makes more sense on the average ship, there is no reason why all those off-duty should not attend. There are good reasons for this. It enables anyone to raise a safety issue and have it discussed, and it enables any new regulations or changes in company or ship procedure to be given to everyone and ensure they understand why. Finally, any safety problems, incidents or accidents will be raised for all to listen to and hopefully learn from.

It is essential that good discipline prevails at such a meeting with matters put forward in an orderly manner, ensuring that the points and questions deal specifically with safety issues rather than meandering off into general shipboard matters. If you are not the safety officer you might have to step in to bring the discussion back on course. Make sure that there is a time limit. Too many see the safety meeting as an excuse to prolong the smoko until mealtime.

It is essential that, at each safety meeting, the drills conducted during the month are discussed and this should be in a critical manner. You should make a good honest assessment of the drills and forward these to the company so that they see an honest record of any problems. You must also be willing to accept any criticism made of your emergency procedures and management, regardless of who it comes from.

Make sure that there is an agenda and stick to it. Any other business can be dealt with after the crew have gone back to work.

Remember that the safety meeting is not intended for a general discussion of all that is wrong in the ship. Nor is it an opportunity to ask for equipment you know you will not get. It is to discuss safety on the ship over the last month, so whoever is the chairman should keep the meeting firmly on track.

21.5 Muster Lists

Fire suits – one size fits all?

When these are being drawn up, try to ensure that the crew selected match the duties they are supposed to perform. A 6'6" hulk is not going to get into a small fire suit no matter how much you try to compress him. Someone who cannot swim and is frightened of the sea is not going to be much good for the rescue boat.

21.6 Drills

Courtesy Fire Aid International

The safety drills are the responsibility of either you or the safety officer, and either way there is a good chance that your influence is the major input onboard. I say this because when the drills are conducted the Master is inevitably on the bridge and he will be relying on your reports about what has been achieved. Always have proper drills that train and prepare your crew. This requires far more effort, use of equipment and time, but it is the only way. Never be tempted to carry out inadequate drills or limited drills while still making the logbook entries.

21.7 Boat Drills

Confidence is only gained through actual use.

Crew must have confidence in their ability to lower the boats and it needs to become a common occurrence so that a certain level of routine can develop. Be careful when assigning every crew member to a certain job as there is no guarantee that they will be available when required. Instead have the essential job in the hands of the seafarers and assign others to tasks as they arrive.

21.8 Survival Suits

Ensure that the crew are familiar with wearing their survival suits and can put them on in the dark on the boat deck. In an emergency, very few crew will hang around in their cabins to do this! Watch them put their lifejackets on and all get into the boat.

If you have a swimming pool then have the crew jump in with their survival suits on. You will be surprised at how many let the water in. This will be caused by either a defective suit, of which there are quite a number, or the suit being worn incorrectly, which is the very common. You must get it across to all onboard that a suit that allows any water to enter is useless. This might not seem so important in warmer waters but, in cold northern conditions, life expectancy in the water will be very short without secure suits.

A final point for you to consider is that if liferafts are used, it is not possible to swim very far in a survival suit without being exhausted and it is extremely difficult for the average person to board a liferaft without assistance.

Every year, if you have a swimming pool, have the crew enter wearing their survival suits.

21.9 Man Overboard Drills

Once again, careful thought about who will do what is essential. Pick your accident boat crew carefully. If you have a rescue boat, there will be those onboard who have training in its use, but be careful as this training will often be only rudimentary. Try, when possible, to get your boats away in port to give the crew experience in handling and the onboard crew experience in launching and recovery. It does help if those in the boat can swim. Apart from stopping them drowning it tends to give them more confidence when working in small boats on the open sea, which is where your boat should be prepared to operate.

21.10 Fire Drills

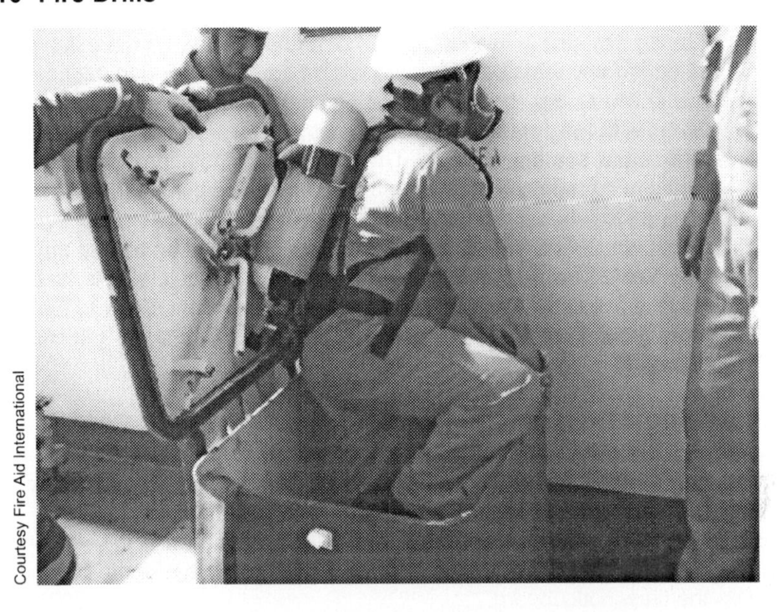

Courtesy Fire Aid International

Your main concern will be the hose and BA set parties, so regular crew should be appointed for them. Familiarisation with the ship can be achieved by holding the fire drill in a different part of the ship each week, sometimes pulling the lighting fuses to simulate smoke. You can order non-toxic, non-staining smoke generators for this purpose and every BA team should practice under such conditions. The foc'sle store is an ideal place for this. Dummies placed beforehand, for crew to bring out, provide good practice. Again, match experience and size with the fire suits.

Once the essential stations are filled the other important functions can be dealt with depending on who you have available. Once again be careful about trying to fill every function with a name. It might be better to have a muster point and then appoint whoever arrives to the most essential task at the time.

During a fire drill, command and control is very important and you must have good communications with the Captain on the bridge and keep him advised of every development. He will be in the position of dealing with all the external communications and trying to make judgement calls based on your information regarding the situation.

Remember that there is a chance that not all crew will be present if an emergency actually occurs. To exercise for this eventuality, occasionally take yourself or any other person out of play and see how the remainder cope with the situation.

21.11 First Aid Drills

This could be an exercise in itself or be part of any other drill, as there is a good chance that during any real situation there will be those suffering from some form of injury. This is where you should consider placing your catering personnel. You must be careful with the personnel in this department. Rarely are they seamen or have the 'sea sense' seamen develop. Think of them as hotel personnel travelling on a ship and use them accordingly or you could be placing them in danger. They should be trained in resuscitation and in treating burns as well as minor injuries. In addition, they should be able to form a stretcher party and be able to manage a stretcher up to the boat deck and into the lifeboats. You could also try to bring a stretcher with a live crew member in it from the engine room plates to the boat deck. This can prove to be quite interesting. Don't forget to give the 'patient' a hard hat, he will need it!

There are many different exercise scenarios for you to develop and the more you challenge the crew's ability the better they will be on the night. After every exercise, you should have an immediate debrief. This is invaluable as all the incidents and what went wrong are still fresh in everyone's minds. Let this discussion be frank, without resentment, and keep a note of what is said. Once you have assessed the points raised write up a brief summary for the Captain and post it on the crew noticeboard.

22 Stores and Storing

This is an extremely important time for any ship, particularly if storing is done on a 3 monthly or, worse, 6 monthly basis. I say worse because it is almost impossible to evaluate needs for months ahead except in the most general terms. The only answer here is to over-order, which you will do anyway, regardless of the storing schedule.

From a management perspective, the best system is where those onboard have a budget and are responsible for ordering their stores. This gives you a choice of where you order, who you order from and what you order. Inevitably, if the opportunity presents itself, you will find that for small orders such as tools you will get better quality and prices from the local shops than from the chandler.

A by-product of having your own budget is that you can appreciate the price of the stores and take better care of them. If your ship husbandry is good you might even have something left over at the end of the financial year to buy a few goodies for the ship. It is wise not to have much left in the kitty as you might find your budget cut for the next year!

To properly order stores you must know what you have onboard. The only way to do this is to make an inventory, unless you happen to have joined a ship with an ongoing inventory system.

When the opportunity arises, generally in poor weather that precludes work on deck, take the opportunity of finding out what stores you have. This can be an enlightening experience, even on a small ship. On a large ship with more places to put things, it can be quite a problem. Usually you are faced with dozens of mops and deck scrubbers for which you have little use and find that the paint you thought you were going to use is years out of date or not compatible with your needs.

The foc'sle usually reveals things that even those onboard have forgotten what they are used for. Drag it all out, keep what you want and what is usable and have the rest ready for disposal. You will also be able to see the condition of the decks, which might in itself be an unpleasant surprise.

You will find that every locker, particularly if the ship is old, will have something to reveal. Having taken your inventory, empty the cabins of their gear. Spanners in drawers, PPE gear stuffed in wardrobes, even your own cabin can have a treasure chest if your predecessor was the 'every finger a marlin spike' type.

22.1 Tools

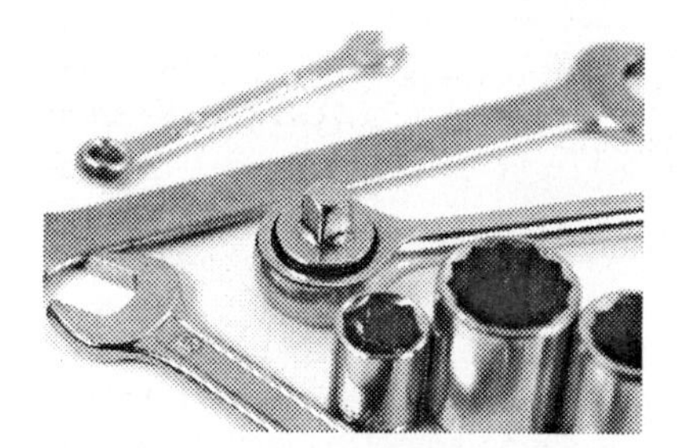

Tools are expensive and need to be looked after.

An unfortunate but frequent attitude about tools is to feel that they are not yours, you didn't pay for them so, if they go missing, order some more. No wonder so many companies get heartily sick of continually paying out for the same tools every stores list. Why is it that a set of screwdrivers can last years ashore, but only months at sea?

The tools belonging to the deck department are nominally in your charge and so it is your job to see that they are looked after. After your clearout you will be surprised at what you have gathered. It should all be listed and then stored to one area. If it is a very large ship there is nothing wrong in establishing two separate stores or workshop areas, forward and aft, as long as you keep track of what belongs where. The best method for tool storage is to draw outline spaces on the painted plyboard. At the end of the day the spaces for tools should be filled again. Be prepared to enforce this. Checking at 2000 hrs when you come off the bridge, and then turning out the crew to find the missing tool, will always get the message across.

22.2 Power Tools

Once again you will come across the 'it's not mine' attitude, which can cause so many problems to the maintenance of the ship. Tools are put aside at the end of the day without being cleaned or, worse, faulty tools are not reported, so that when they are next needed they fail. If this is the pattern you find you must instil a more careful attitude in your crew. Power tools and their spares should be kept apart in their own separate boxes and cleaned after use. They should be part of your maintenance programme. If there is no written procedure laid down for this, establish your own.

22.3 Disposable Items

A little care can save on ordering and expense.

These are items such as paintbrushes, rollers, deck brooms, mops buckets etc. For some reason the word disposable seems to have reached new heights at sea, with crew translating this into 'one use only'. Paint the deck then bung the roller in the trash can instead of cleaning it!

22.4 A Storekeeper

Many years ago, when we had properly sized crew for the size of the ship, in addition to the Bosun a storekeeper, or lamp trimmer as he could be called, was carried and it was his duty to look after the stores, issue them, collect them and care for them. He was the one who got the paint and equipment ready in the morning so that you could immediately start a job without wasting time getting ready. At the end of the day he was the one who cleaned the gear, such as paint brushes, and stowed them away ready for the next use, ensuring that the crew could work right to the end of the day instead of sloping off and spending 30 minutes 'cleaning'.

The value of such a man cannot be overestimated. I would suggest that, if the size of your crew allows, you consider designating one of the crew to take on this position. It does not mean that he is lost for the day, just that he starts a little earlier to prepare the paint, tools or whatever is required for that day and then, in the evening, continues a little longer cleaning and stowing the equipment away. If you are unable to pay overtime, you could compensate him for the extra work in time off when the other crew are working. At least then you are going to have your equipment looked after and have someone responsible for it. The other option is to have the Bosun take on this responsibility. Either way, if you are going to have the job done, someone will have to be responsible.

22.5 The Running Inventory

Once you have your store rooms, cupboards and lockers emptied out and all the rubbish discarded, it makes sense, while you are putting the stores back, to try to separate the items. Put the cleaning and domestic in one, maintenance in another and tools in another. On the back of the door or access make out a printed list of the items in that particular store with a space for the number of each item present, those issued, those received and those remaining. If you can train your crew, or whoever is the storekeeper, to maintain these lists, it will provide you with an indication of the stores you are using and their consumption rate. This is important when you are making up your stores order.

22.6 Stores Ordering

The Captain or Chief Engineer will probably assemble the full list of stores required if sending to the company or putting out to a chandler for pricing. In addition to your own list you will need to collect the requirements of the Bosun, the navigating officer and whoever is dealing with medical supplies. If you are looking after the catering department general stores you will need the requirements of the Chief Cook as well.

Laziness often creeps into this ordering, so the fact that they have ordered 12 mops and 200 bars of soap every 6 months for the last 5 years will account for the fact that you have a locker somewhere onboard containing over one hundred mops and a few thousand bars of soap. Individually these are not expensive items, but collectively they are a waste of money in stores not required and money tied up in carrying unwanted goods across the world and back. It is not your money either, which is probably why this situation occurs. At least by emptying your storerooms you will have found the soap and mops and will not be ordering any more for a while!

22.7 Storing Procedures

The location where you take on stores will affect which stores you receive and what their condition is. The perfect situation is one where you can specify the time you will receive the stores, where you have a berth that your stores crane can reach because the berth storing area is free from obstructions, the weather is good and you have sufficient time in the port for stores to be checked and missing or defective items replaced. I can already hear some Chief Officers muttering 'in your dreams'!

To have such conditions is almost unheard of. Many berths or terminals are not 'ship friendly'. Some even refuse to allow crew to store the ship or use the ship's crane. In other ports the crane will not reach or it is on the wrong side, the rain is pouring down, the berth is covered in coal dust and the ship is sailing in a few hours. You could be struggling at night to load your stores from a boat while under way through the Singapore Straits. Whatever the difficulties, you must manage the situation and somehow get the stores onboard.

The problems arising from this type of storing are numerous, not the least of which is that stores often disappear into the ship without being checked properly. The hammers that you cannot find will appear a month later from the linen store and the screwdrivers that are so essential have disappeared into the engine room. Wrongly supplied items often cannot be returned for replacement.

If you know when your ship is berthing and roughly know your ETD, then at least you can specify when the stores are to be delivered. It is guaranteed that, whatever time you state, they will arrive during a mealtime!

23 Bridge Duties

23.1 Watchkeeping

Traditionally, the Chief Officer carries out the 4-8 watch unless lucky enough to be on daywork, but be careful of the tendency for the more senior officer to become a little blasé about standing on the bridge for 8 hours a day.

You must have confidence in your abilities, but you should always be ready for the unexpected. Your conduct on the bridge will probably be governed by the Captain's standing orders and, like my own in later years, these may well specify the distance at which you are to pass other vessels. This is not because of distrust in your team's abilities, but in those of the other ship.

A recent study into manning and fatigue at sea found:

- *A high proportion of those sampled reported having been in collision with ships or objects*
- *nearly half of those sampled considered fatigue to be a key factor in reducing collision awareness*
- *one in four watchkeepers (especially those on longer watches) reported having fallen asleep on watch*
- *almost all watchkeepers were required to do multi-tasking while on watch*
- *those engaged in multi-tasking were found to be more likely to fall asleep on watch.*

The most common suggestion to help provide more effective and alert watchkeeping is to improve the manning.

Does the manning certificate reflect the reality of the vessel and trade?

The manning level requirements are noted in the British Merchant Shipping Notice No. 1767, but it must be emphasised that these are for *guidance only*.

The manning guidance for a near coastal vessel of between 500 gt and 3000 gt is the Master and one other.

If the vessel is under 500 gt for unlimited trading it is the same. However, for near coastal vessels under 500 gt, less stringent requirements apply.

It is difficult to understand any reasoning except commercial pressure that allows such a difference to exist between near coastal and unlimited trading vessels, irrespective of size, particularly as coastal ships are operating in denser traffic conditions requiring a high watchkeeping standard.

The TNO report (Houtman et al, 2005) on 'Fatigue in the Shipping Industry', highlights the priority measure to reduce fatigue as to replace the two watch system with a three watch system, by use of an additional watchkeeper.

In section 94 of the British Merchant Shipping Act, it states that a ship is 'dangerously unsafe' if, in regard to the nature of the service for which it is intended, the ship is by reason of various matters specified unfit to go to sea without serious danger to human life. One of those matters is undermanning.

In a review of the international literature on seafarers' fatigue, one of the main messages was:

'Evidence shows that seafarers' shift and work patterns are often conducive to fatigue. Having only two bridge watchkeepers may be a particular problem'.

In the Marine Accident Investigation Branch 'Bridge Watchkeeping Safety Study 2004', it was concluded that watchkeeper manning levels are one of the causative factors in collisions and groundings and the report recommends that:

'In general, vessels over 500 gt should have a minimum of the Master and two watchkeeping officers onboard'.

While welcoming this recommendation I would ask the question that, if the Master is part of the watchkeeping of the ship, who is in charge and supervising the operation of the ship? The system was designed to be based on watchkeepers and a Master who is on call at all times. Therefore, when the ship enters fog or any other problematic situation, the Master is available to double up the bridge, increasing the vigilance and safety. Instead we now have the situation of large vessels proceeding through the channel and other confined waters, in fog, with just one officer on the bridge and the Master sleeping after his watch.

Next, why this fixation with 500 gt ships? Such a ship surely requires the same care as any other? A ship of that size or under, in collision with vessels far larger, can sink them just as certainly as any other. Time and time again we see conclusions and findings that seem to be driven by financial influences rather than cold hard facts.

23.2 Lookouts

Can smaller ships in coastal areas justify fewer watchkeepers?

As the Chief Officer you could find yourself in a difficult situation. If you are on a vessel with only the Master and yourself you should constantly have lookouts on the bridge as you will experience fatigue from port work and then a six hour watch.

Yet the ship could well only have two or three ratings. How are you supposed to keep these men on the bridge and carry out all the other work required in the ship, whether it is general cleaning duties or essential preparation for port arrival?

Even on larger ships, with the amount of work required it is very tempting for both the Master and the Chief Officer, when deep sea, to dispense with the lookouts in return for a larger available workforce. The regulations do allow for the lookout on the bridge to be engaged on other duties during daylight hours, provided that he is instantly available to the OOW. The word 'available' is open to a varied interpretation. Personally, I fail to understand why there is any differential between day and night as this completely ignores the advances of electronic aids available today. However, the speed of vessels in low visibility and the removal of many fixed navigational aids from the coasts ***does*** recognise that.

On the question of lookouts, it is illogical to differentiate between day and night. If a lookout is required at night then a lookout is required in the day. It is rare for any watchkeeper to detect a ship or danger to navigation visually before the radar, while at night, the OOWs keep a better watch on the radar. By contrast, the bridge tends to be far busier during the day than the night, with extra tasks and distractions. The case, therefore, is stronger for lookouts to be appointed during the day.

We should sensibly have, for adequate watchkeeping and compliance with the lookout regulations, a minimum of three watchkeeping officers and three ratings and these should be recognised as the minimum bridge watchkeeping requirement, regardless of the size of ship. The difficulties of establishing such a regime must be recognised. In the EU zone alone we would need at least 3,000 extra seafarers, at a time when there are already shortages, and there is generally insufficient accommodation onboard for such additions. But these difficulties should not stop us from establishing policy and working towards international agreement, ensuring that all future manning certificates reflect these obligations. For existing ships with a lack of available crew or accommodation, exemptions could be granted and, with these exemptions, clauses could be included about the hours of work onboard and hiring of extra labour in the ports to ease the problems.

I believe that we are a long way from seeing such a position but, as the accidents continue, the pressure will grow. Meanwhile you have urgent work to be done, you are short of men and you have regulations to follow. It is conceivable you may feel the only answer is to go to the Master and request that, as you are crossing the ocean with very little traffic, you be allowed to stand down the lookouts. The Master may even suggest this to you.

However, you are putting the Master in a difficult position. He understands the difficulties you are having with getting the work done yet, if he has any sense, he recognises that by removing the lookouts he is not only breaking the regulations but, to a degree, putting the vessel into a more dangerous position. If the Master suggests such a course he is failing in his responsibilities.

Whatever the temptation, the lack of traffic or the pressures from any quarter, keep your lookouts as per the regulations. I will go further; you should ensure that any request during the day from the other watchkeeping officers for lookouts is seriously considered without any recrimination. By asking for them, they are proving that they have the sense to feel concerned.

A final thought regarding lookouts, particularly on the coast. Consider the distractions that are occurring on the bridge with communications, visitors and the mobile telephone and ensure that you have a lookout present who is not doing anything but keeping lookout!

If you are in a situation with only two ratings, or where you feel that your ship is not manned properly to be able to comply both with the fatigue and lookout regulations, without hesitation write a letter to the Marine Administration of the Flag state as they are responsible for the manning. If you have done this and subsequently there is an accident resulting from a lack of lookouts, let them answer the consequences in court, not you. Only by the actions of responsible seafarers at sea comes the realisation that the situation on many ships is now critical and must be dealt with.

23.3 The Deck Logbook

The deck logbook is a legal document and must be treated as such. It is not, however, a sacred book in which only certain defined items such as navigation can be written. It is a living diary of the affairs of any importance that occur during the voyage. Therefore, you should think in terms of personal injuries, damage to the ship, oil noted in the waters, in fact anything that might need to be cited or explained at a later date. Do not forget that documents or statements can be attached to a logbook entry, provided they have been dated and signed.

Be careful about backdating entries. They are often easy to spot and just one such proven entry can render your logbook suspect in the eyes of any court or inquiry. Initialled crossings out are better than alterations.

With regard to the weather, it is perfectly reasonable to enter the highest wind force and sea state that occurred during the watch. If you have a rapidly changing situation, enter the weather conditions for each hour.

Do not forget the standard entries that should be made, such as safety rounds, hatches secured, all navigation gear tested, steering tests, clocks synchronised and engines tested prior to arrival.

24 Alcohol

While many people enjoy alcohol, it is when it becomes a 'need', that it becomes dangerous. Everyone concerned with regulation must consider alcohol and its effects, and as the Chief Officer you will need to be involved in this.

24.1 Bars

Whether or not alcohol is permitted on your vessel is the decision of your company. How it is tolerated onboard is the decision of the Captain and you are responsible to him for enforcing his wishes. The bars, both crew and officers', are nominally under your control. In days gone by, you would have had the title of 'president' of the wardroom or officers' bar. Although this title may have disappeared, the responsibility has not.

The best way to control the bars is to appoint a committee to be responsible to you for the running and good order of each. The committee should consist of:

- A chairman
- a bar manager
- crew or officers' representative
- on larger ships, an entertainment representative.

You can lay down the guidelines for the good order of the bars. Most important of these will be the bar hours, which must be sensible and not conflict with the working hours of the ship or the sleep of nearby watchkeepers.

24.2 Record Keeping of Alcohol Consumption

It is essential that any bar keeps a record of who is drinking what, and it is easy for alcohol to be sold on a book basis where those consuming enter what they are buying in a book under their name. It is a system based on honesty and, while occasionally abused, it is generally only through forgetfulness rather than systematic theft. If it is abused too much, as all those using the bar will have to make up the difference if the bar is to remain open, it is in their interests to find the culprit.

24.3 The Behaviour of those in the Bar, and Guests

Opening and closing hours will be decided by the Captain and those running it will be responsible for ensuring the hours are kept to. There is nothing wrong with an occasional extension being granted, but this should be applied for in advance.

The behaviour of those using the bar is usually subject to self-regulation, but if this fails discipline will need to be imposed.

The same applies for any guests. The responsibility for guests lies completely with the person who invited them and they must be removed from the bar if it is judged by others present that their behaviour is not suitable.

24.4 The Crew Bar

It would make sense that the Bosun is the chairman in the crew bar unless he violently objects to this. Either way it should be a crew member of petty officer level to give him the authority to deal with any problems. The bar enables alcohol to be controlled onboard, with the closure of the bar as a constant threat for any abuse of the system.

24.5 Mixing

In my view, the mixing of officers and crew in the bars is to be discouraged. Obviously, times such as birthdays and darts matches, etc, are occasions for mixing to occur, with the benefit to the ship in general, but that is sufficient.

I always found that the crew generally do not want the officers in their bar and I remember on one occasion being called by the Bosun to go down and tell some officers to remove themselves from the crew bar.

24.6 Bringing Alcohol Onboard

If you have bars onboard, then under no circumstances should you allow alcohol to be brought onto the ship for private consumption. There will usually be a regulation regarding this through the company SMS but, if there is not, advise the Captain of your intentions and, with his support, distribute this message to the ship and brief your officers and the gangway watch about your attitude to this.

If necessary, you can use bar closure to emphasise the seriousness of any flouting of this rule.

24.7 Banning Alcohol

If there is no alcohol permitted onboard then you may have a problem. Certainly in the west and in many parts of Asia, alcohol is part of the social scene. When it is removed from the ship those who are accustomed to it feel a deep loss and their sociability may be affected. Morale within the ship suffers and those who do drink will wish to do so no matter what rules your company wishes to impose.

This can have a drastic effect on the efficiency and discipline of the ship. First it means that, in every port regardless of the distance, some of the crew will go ashore when in the past they were content to stay onboard. It also means that some will overindulge when they find a bar or alcohol. Many will attempt to bring alcohol back onboard.

As Chief Officer, you now have several problems. First you will have crew smuggling drink onboard, and no matter how hard you try, you will not stop this. Even if you stand on the gangway during the entire time in port they will ask the shore workers to bring it for them, and you certainly do not have the authority to search the shore workers. So now you have drink onboard for cabin drinking.

Next, you have the problem of an inebriated crew coming back onboard, which can occur just before sailing meaning they should not be undertaking any duty. Now we know the paper answer, which is that, if they are essential to the sailing of the ship, you do not sail until they are sober. However, the real answer for many ships is that, with the pressure of the port and charterer's threat of putting the ship off-hire if it waits, the ship sails.

I recall as a young cadet watching a crew trying to make the foc'sle when some idiot in the company had decided to sail the ship just after midnight on New Year's Day. It was a sight to behold as various bodies gently subsided on the deck on the way forward. A sufficient number made it so we could sail, even if a little unsteadily as the bridge wasn't much better.

25 Discipline

We are generally very fortunate on merchant ships as, regardless of the registry, the kind of seafarers who sail on the ships are, surprising to those ashore, just as law abiding as their shore counterparts. To sail on ships where a number of people who come together from differing backgrounds and cultures and nationalities are compressed together in a small community for months on end, discipline is the essential fabric that holds the ship together, particularly self-discipline. Only very occasionally do we have to fall back on imposed regulation and the threat of punishment but, as in society ashore, this must still be the final recourse.

It is very important that discipline is seen as fair, even handed and applied with sense. If an engine room rating and a deck rating roll back to the ship at 0830 in the morning when the working day starts at 0800, you cannot discipline the deck rating if the engine rating is not dealt with in the same way. This means that you must establish a policy between the departments. If this cannot be done, these offences would have to be placed before the Master, which then makes it all a bit too official. Of course, the level of discipline and punishment depends on the Captain and you must seek his guidance at an early stage to find out his wishes. Once he passes them to you it is for you to pass them on to the ship, particularly the Bosun, and ensure that they are complied with. The main thing with discipline is to remain on top of it. No one should go to the Captain with any problem, except through you.

This is not for the purpose of hiding things from the command, but to ensure that the complainants have a case and that there is no unofficial way that it can be dealt with, to a better outcome of all concerned.

It is important that your authority is accepted. If the rules say no smoking in the messroom then, should you enter and see someone smoking, you must enforce the regulation. The same applies to the rest of the ship. If you are seen from the beginning as a no nonsense Chief Officer who will enforce the company's or Master's regulations onboard, you will be respected provided that the level of discipline is even and fair.

Dealing with the officers is harder. You cannot allow officers to break regulations, but it would be appropriate and courteous to advise the Chief Engineer over his departmental officers' misconduct so that he can take action. If this is done and no action is taken, you will have to move to the next level, which is the Captain. You really do not want to do this and I am sure that the Chief Engineer doesn't want this either, so hopefully a small discussion regarding any discipline problems will ensure cooperation.

25.1 Warnings

As the head of department, it is normal for you to issue informal and written warnings for minor infractions of the ship's regulations. This can be done on your own initiative, or at the request of the heads of other departments, where certain behaviour or actions warrant it. When such action is taken, you should advise the Master, not just to keep him informed but, in the case of a written warning, he may wish to enter the matter into the official log-book if you have one onboard. When you issue an official warning, make sure that you have a witness or witnesses and that the defaulter has a copy of it. A record should also be made of any verbal reply.

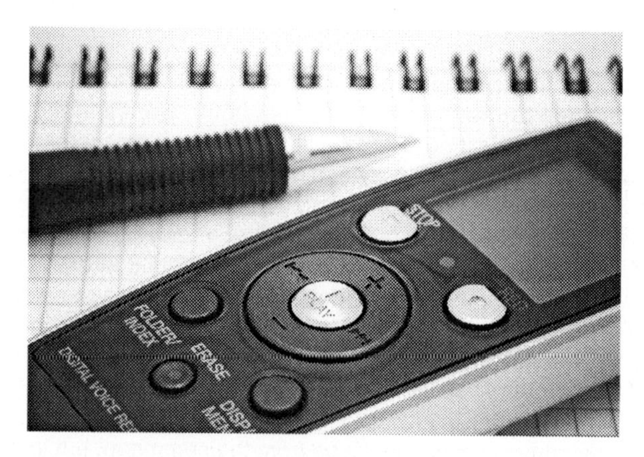

This is where your voice recorder will be of good use.

Quite often this will be your first experience of acting in the role of disciplinarian and giving judgement. If this is the case, you must ensure that at all times you are acting fairly and that the reasons warrant your intervention. Verbal and written warnings can be given to officers as well and there may be times when you have to resort to such action to get a point across. Warnings must be given by the head of the department concerned.

Another type of warning that is not unknown is the 'pencil' warning. This is done by the Master and is really the last resort before formal punishment proceedings. If you have a situation where formal warnings have been given and another offence has been committed then you can request the Master to issue a pencil warning if you feel that the case still does not warrant full punishment. Be aware that the Captain may well feel that a full recorded punishment is warranted and carry on regardless! Should the pencil 'logging' be given, it is exactly the same as a full logbook offence hearing except that the entry in the logbook is made in pencil with the proviso that, if there are no further problems, at the end of the person's contract it will be erased from the ship's records and no mention of it will be made on any personal record.

25.2 Serious Offences

Your Flag state will have a list of offences and the punishments allowed under their laws. You have some leeway in prescribing a lesser punishment, but you cannot do more. For serious offences that merit more than is stated by the Flag state, the offender has to be sent ashore at a convenient port for that country's authorities to deal with. The whole question of crime and punishment at sea on a ship is murky to say the least. Even Flag states with proper marine administrations prefer you to deal with any problems, although at times this is clearly not possible.

While this is the Captain's area of responsibility, you should consider some of the issues that you may be placing before him.

25.3 Disobedience

The disobedience of any command or insolent behaviour to an officer on a ship is a direct challenge to the authority of the Captain, you and the officers and must be dealt with regardless of the circumstances. The way it is dealt with depends on the situation, but if left without resolution it will fester between those involved and may erupt at a future date, possibly with a loss of authority.

When an officer comes to you with a complaint regarding disobedience, you must sort out if it really is an offence or if it is the officer's fault through not giving a clearly defined order. Is the order legal? 'Jump over the side Harry and get my cap' is not an order I would obey, nor would you. Sort out the truth first before deciding what to do. There are times when an offence occurs and can be sorted out with a warning. This is your decision but if you feel uneasy about any matter take it to the Captain. Whatever you do, do not ignore it.

While on the subject of orders, never give an order that you know will not be obeyed. In other words, don't put a person in a corner. Always leave the door open for a way out. Giving an order that you know will not be carried out diminishes your authority.

25.4 Theft

There are three types of theft that occur on a ship: theft of cargo, theft of stores and theft of personal effects. All of these can occur in port or at sea, but most of them will occur in port where it is difficult to fix the blame either on the crew or shore workers.

Theft from the cargo rarely occurs at sea, particularly with containers, although it is not unheard of.

Theft of stores is almost a normal occurrence. This is not to say that you accept it, but it is part of sea life. In the past, when there was a crew change, all the baggage of the leaving crew was searched at the gangway and the haul was usually quite good.

Personal theft is the one that causes most problems as suspicion and accusations can disrupt a ship. It is also very hard to deal with because, unless the thief is caught in the act or with the stolen property, it can go on for months. Searching cabins will generally do no good as the stolen items will often be secreted away somewhere on the ship and any hint of a search can often cause the items to be discarded over the side.

Where theft is discovered or reported to you, it must immediately be reported to the Captain for his decision on the matter. What you have to ensure is that, if the theft is of cargo or stores, then action is taken to ensure their future security. If it is personal theft, there must be no stupid accusations or actions taken against any suspects.

25.5 Assault

On a ship, you may be involved in three types of assault and quite often in the repairs afterwards. The first is a thump between friends with everyone sorry afterwards. If you hear of this unofficially and there is no damage done to ship or person, then leave it that way.

The second is an assault deliberately made on a superior or by an officer on someone junior to him, both equally serious. This can only be dealt with by the Captain and, depending on the circumstances, he can warrant the involvement of shore authorities.

A serious but fortunately rare occurrence onboard.

The third is an assault with a weapon, in my experience usually involving a knife or a bottle. Great care is needed when dealing with such a case. As the Chief Officer, you will be called immediately and could soon find yourself in a situation where the assailant is still armed and in a highly agitated state. The main concern must be avoiding any casualty and getting everyone away from the assailant as their presence may be encouraging him, possibly provoking his ego into further acts of defiance. If necessary, leave him alone. He is not going anywhere unless it is over the side.

By now the ship's 'doctor' will be there, dealing with the first aid, and the Master could be there too. However, you could be left with the job of dealing with the culprit. There are, no doubt, many proposed ways of dealing with such a problem, but it is my experience that if you can reduce the confrontational element the situation improves. Most assaults occur in anger and quite often the culprit is frightened of what he has done and agitated over the consequences.

I had to deal with three such incidents, all as Chief Officer, the worst involving a broken bottle. In each case, I ordered everyone else away, leaving us both together. Then I sat down and asked if he would like to sit and talk about it. I assured them that there was no real harm done and that if the weapon was put down and they went to their cabin we would deal with the problem after a rest.

Never try to take a weapon away from someone. Ask them to put it down on a table or the deck and go to their cabin.

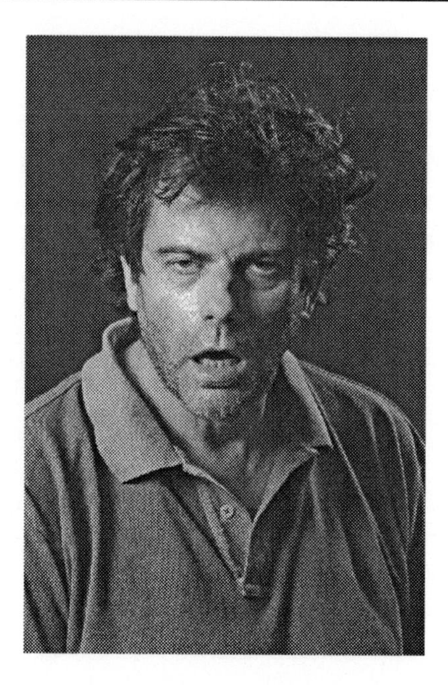

This is not the time to discipline someone.

Remove the fear and the agitation and you are mostly home. Do think about this though, as there is a good chance that, in your time as Chief Officer, you may have to deal with confronting someone with a weapon. You are the Mate, this is your job.

When the culprit has gone to his cabin, put someone on his door and have him checked periodically to ensure that he is not harming himself. Under no circumstances try to discipline him while he is still agitated.

25.6 Drunkenness

This is something that as seamen we are or should be quite familiar with, particularly with crews from countries that have an alcohol tolerance. Most of us from such countries have been drunk ourselves, particularly in our youth.

As we know, there are differing degrees of drunkenness. An alcoholic can hide it well but is very dangerous, as he can go about his normal duties in such a state without anyone recognising his condition until it is too late.

One chief Engineer I sailed with behaved strangely but we put this down to his personality. His condition only came to light when we ran out of spirits in the bond. No one worried too much except he became agitated and then, after a day or so, he had the shakes. It transpired that his bond issue remained within reason as he had all the engineer officers drawing bond for him. There are not so many alcoholics at sea these days, but some are still around, surprisingly sometimes with the company's knowledge!

There is the happy drunk who just becomes stupid. Hopefully, when he staggers onboard and gives everyone a kiss he will disappear to his cabin and sleep it off. Better to be discreetly out of the way and turn a blind eye.

Finally there is the belligerent drunk who wants to sort out the ship, the world and anyone he sees. Once again don't try to argue, just let him get to his bunk. If there is no one to argue with he will go to bed.

Generally, when crew come back onboard it is a time for 'authority' to be discreetly absent unless there is a problem. Always be wary though, not for you, but for them. If they are very drunk you might have to put them where they can be watched owing to the possibility that they will vomit in their sleep and choke.

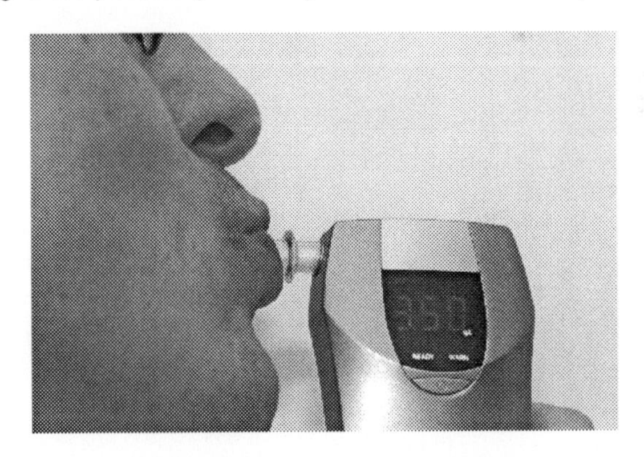

Hopefully an unnecessary deterant.

Being drunk on duty is a different story and it cannot be tolerated. If a member of the ship's company is suspected of being intoxicated he must immediately be stood down from whatever task he is doing and given a breath test. Should he refuse to take this then the assumption must be made that he is under the influence and he must be sent to his cabin. Under no circumstances can he return to duty. When sober, he must be brought before the Captain, regardless of his rating or rank.

25.7 Drugs

There are very good publications around regarding this issue and I suggest that you read them. In my experience drugs on ships are rare, unless it is a cruise ship when many of the passengers bring them onboard or buy them from the crew or in the ports of call.

The books deal well with how to recognise those using drugs and if you suspect anyone being under the influence then they must be removed from duty.

If somebody has brought drugs on for profit, they will not generally be kept in the cabin of the carrier, but will be stowed somewhere safe on the ship. Be careful what you do should drugs be found in such a quantity that they are obviously being carried for delivery. If no one else knows of their discovery keep it that way. When the Master is advised of their presence, and he informs the coastguard of them and the fact that no one knows of the discovery, there is a very good chance that the officials at the port of delivery will want to track them from the ship to the consignee. At least your actions will give them that option.

25.8 Bullying

This is worth a mention, although I have seldom seen systematic bullying on a ship. Yes there is the usual teasing of new seafarers or cadets, but this is mostly done in good humour. The larger the crew, the more chance of bullying occurring so it is worth keeping your eye open for it. The Bosun will know if it is happening, so make sure he knows your attitude to it. Watch out for over exuberance on the Bosun's part as well. A hard Bosun often walks a thin line between ordering and bullying but there are not too many hard Bosuns left.

26 Enclosed Space Entry

Any death from enclosed space entry on a ship is pointless and a terrible waste of life. A lot has been said about this subject in books, DVDs, SMSs and company memos and yet it still happens. Make sure it does not on your ship.

My one experience of this was when I was a cadet. We were finishing smoko ready to go down into an oil tank that had been opened early that morning. The carpenter was having coffee with us and told us to take our time finishing the coffee and that he would go on and get things ready in the tank. We thought no more about it until we arrived at the top of the tank and, looking down, saw his body. Luckily the senior cadet stopped any attempt to enter the tank and called for assistance. The Chief Officer duly arrived and, using the BA set, the corpse was hooked up to the crane and lifted out.

That incident has always stood out in my memory and I am pleased to say I have never had any accident during my time as Chief Officer or Captain.

I think one problem with enclosed spaces is in their definition and the difficulty of those on the ship to distinguish between shore and sea. After all, who mentions or worries about enclosed spaces ashore. Does Granny think twice before going in the coal shed? I remember a sanitary worker wanting to go into a cesspit on my property and was quite bemused when I prevented him until it had been completely ventilated.

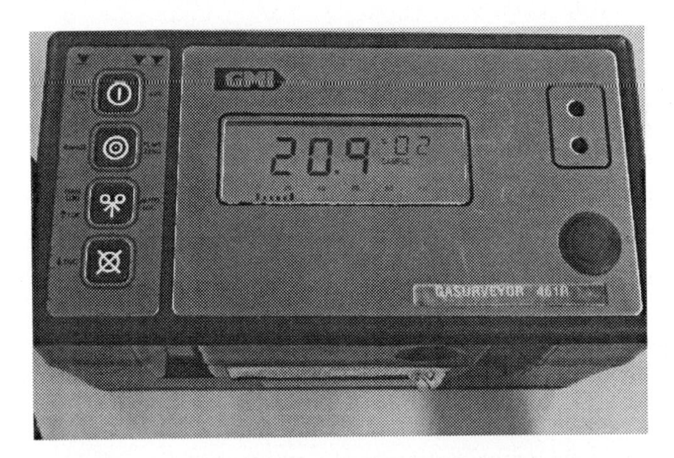

I am not going to enumerate all the precautions here but will ask that you think about fresh air, which is a basic requirement to the functioning of our bodies. A human being requires an atmosphere of 20.9% oxygen and 78% nitrogen for wellbeing. Any space that has less that 20.9% oxygen is dangerous and will eventually be fatal. Most substances give off gases of some kind or other, even the bulkheads of an empty space can do that, so any space that has been closed for some time without any ventilation must be considered dangerous.

Somehow you must get this through to those onboard. Following a rigorous risk assessment will certainly help, but familiarity tends to creep into this system unless you insist upon it. The oxygen meter should be a normal part of equipment for crew and all crew should be required to operate and understand it. One day, in the distant future, all enclosed spaces onboard ship will have an automatic detection and warning system, but at the moment this is not the case so we have to rely on our common sense. Work on the principle that all spaces that have been closed for any period of time, especially those with seals such as tanks and stores with weather or storm doors, are potentially dangerous.

Finally, establish a list of all enclosed spaces on the ship, even what may be considered stupid places, such as the broom cupboard. Then make a risk assessment for each and every space with colour coding. The broom cupboard can be graded as safe and need not be of concern, unless toxic cleaning fluids are also stored there, but any other spaces with higher grades must require care. The higher the grade the more care. For all spaces requiring care put the colour grade on the door. Permission must be obtained from the bridge to enter certain specific colour graded compartments. The bridge will keep a list of these spaces and each time they are entered will log the date so that the ship has a record. Very quickly it will become apparent which compartments are seldom entered and, therefore, which are the most dangerous. All this might seem a nuisance but, if it saves a life, it is surely worth the bother.

This is that just a suggestion to try to deal with the problem in a way safeguards a new and unwary crew member, as he is the most vulnerable. Of course, a storeroom that is categorised safe and then has a chemical spilled inside, giving off toxic gases, can be lethal to anyone entering.

26.1 Enhanced Survey Programme

Although the tanks will be surveyed by Class as part of this programme, many companies now require them to go through a periodic survey by the ship's staff. Obviously, this inspection is not as thorough as that done by the Class surveyors, but it does mean that if there is any major problem developing it should be identified.

Entering the tanks to inspect for corrosion and cracking of the steelwork is a filthy job taking up a considerable amount of your time. It is very tempting to simply tick the box but this inspection is very important, particularly on older ships. There are certain precautions you must take. Good ventilation is essential, as are detection meters for oxygen and other gases. Never enter on your own, and ensure that at the top of the access there is a crewman standing by. The personal communicators you carry may not work well in such spaces so ensure that there is a chain of communication that keeps you in touch with the deck. Have a BA set standing by in case this is needed.

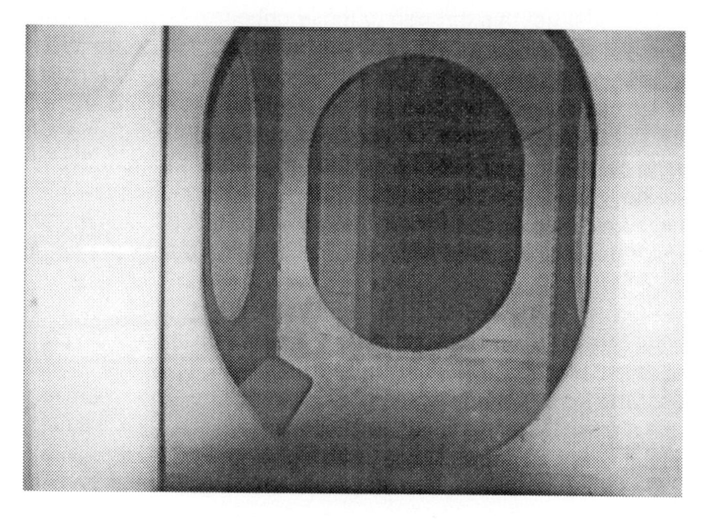

If you have never entered the tanks of a double hulled vessel before it can be a strange experience, particularly when on 300,000 dwt ships. It is like a vast coalmine divided into a multitude of sections with crawl through lightening holes and, after a few sections you are in a dark silent world under the sea. Rather than a note-book, take a voice recorder, as it is not easy to write in such conditions, particularly with working gloves on. Ensure that your beam lights are newly charged. It is very unpleasant to find yourself in pitch black darkness in such a place. Identify the sections, by a sequence of letters and match these to the plans when you emerge. Take a surveyor's hammer with you to knock the scale away to look for cracks.

Don't be taken in by the scale. Recently, on a small 500 dwt ship we took out 5 tons of scale from two tanks and still the steelwork was acceptable. It is stress cracks that you are really looking for.

Enclosed Space Entry Checklist

- ☑ Is it necessary?
- ☑ Are the instruments used in atmospheric testing properly calibrated?
- ☑ Was the atmosphere in the confined space tested?
- ☑ Was oxygen at least 20.9% - not more than 21%? (Note: That, while 20.9 is value often quoted, 20.8 is the value typically quoted on a work permit)
- ☑ Were toxic, flammable or oxygen-displacing gases/vapours present?
  - Hydrogen sulphide ppm
  - Carbon monoxide ppm
  - Methane LEL
  - Carbon dioxide ppm
- ☑ Will the atmosphere in the space be monitored while work is going on?
- ☑ Has the space been ventilated before entry?
- ☑ Will ventilation be continued during entry?
- ☑ Is the air intake for the ventilation system located in an area that is free of combustible dusts and vapours and toxic substances?
- ☑ Has the space been isolated from other systems?
- ☑ Has electrical equipment been locked out?
- ☑ Have lines under pressure been blanked and bled?
- ☑ Is special clothing required (boots, chemical suits, glasses, etc)?
- ☑ Is special equipment required (eg rescue equipment, communications equipment etc)?
- ☑ Are special tools required (eg spark proof)?
- ☑ Is respiratory protection required (eg air-purifying, supplied air, self-contained breathing apparatus, etc)?
- ☑ Will there be a standby person on the outside in constant visual or auditory communication with the person inside?
- ☑ Will the standby person be able to see and/or hear the person inside at all times?
- ☑ Has the standby person(s) been trained in rescue procedures?
- ☑ Will safety lines and harness be required to remove a person?
- ☑ Are you familiar with emergency rescue procedures?
- ☑ Do you know who and how to notify in the event of an emergency?
- ☑ Has a confined space entry permit been issued?

27 Communication

Telling people what is happening, finding out their views and discussing your ideas helps considerably in understanding them and in them understanding you. No one is a mind reader and constant communication is necessary when dealing with and relating to problems and situations.

You must be seen as the man that people can talk to, either on a professional basis or a personal level. Do not talk about other people behind their backs unless it is something good. Finally, a sense of humour is essential for anyone aspiring to leadership. If there is a funny side to a situation then see it, at the appropriate time of course!

27.1 With the Office

The fact that the Chief Officer can read and write can come as a surprise to some companies. There seems to be an attitude that all communications must come from the Master or the Chief Engineer. This can be frustrating, but there is nothing to stop you from asking the Master if you can send off your own e-mails to both the company and to the port regarding the cargo planning, with copies sent to the Master.

All letters from the ship must be countersigned by the Master. Remember that anything sent cannot easily be retrieved, so leave anything written in anger until the morning.

27.2 With the Captain

I always used to look forward to talking with the Captain in the mornings when he visited the bridge to have a tea or coffee. This discussion at the beginning of the day, before the work started, was the best time for reviewing the ship and any problems. The bridge was a neutral place and avoided the more formal atmosphere of his office or cabin. If you can, try to encourage such meetings.

27.3 With the Crew

It is often assumed by the senior officers that the crew know what is going on. Without a doubt the galley radio works well but it also has a habit of making up news that doesn't exist. If there is anything of interest regarding the ship, future movements or cargoes or changes of crew, in fact anything that might affect them, then tell the crew. A short one page newsletter on their noticeboard is an excellent way to keep them informed. They will still believe what they hear on the galley radio, but at least you will have tried!

27.4 With the Officers

Talking is a great medium. It saves writing, can clear up misunderstandings and stop loneliness. Just finding out where they come from, what they are doing at sea and asking after their family provides a break to what can be for some a lonely environment. If an officer is not doing well, you might find out why and get the opportunity to informally help.

You can only know each other by talking to each other. Too often with a mixed crew everyone settles into their own cultural groups. As the Chief Officer, regardless of your nationality, you have to be open to all.

28 Port Preparation

28.1 Planning

A ship arriving in port without a plan is a management disaster in the making. Although I am not too happy with the reception some shore authorities give to ships, when you understand what they have to deal with at times you may have a little more sympathy for their behaviour.

If there is no planning meeting on your ship at least ensure that your own responsibilities are well prepared for.

28.2 Cargo

The most important item on your agenda will be the cargo.

You will need to submit your cargo stowage plan. Ensure that you do this in sufficient time for any changes that are necessary to be made prior to arrival. Once the Master has declared the stability condition he requires for sailing and arrival at the port of destination, you can finalise your requirements and send this off to the agent. Allow for weekends in your timings as, if your plan arrives on a Friday afternoon, it can quite possibly lie in the agency office for the whole weekend and only be forwarded to the port or terminal on the Monday. This does not help anyone if you are arriving on Monday morning.

If you are on a cargo ship, you want to know what hatches they intend to start with first, if there is an option.

28.3 Stores

Regardless of the 3 or 6 monthly storing, there always seem to be items that are urgently required. Ensure that your department advises you of any such stores well before the port so that you can assess their requirement and advise the Master in case he has to obtain the company's permission.

Some years ago, on a ship operated by a well known Scottish ship management company, the crew kettle broke and could not be repaired. In this company every item had to be approved by head office so I went to the Captain with my request. First I had the inquisition. Why had the kettle broken, who broke it, why could it not be repaired, did I realise that the kettle was only ten years old and still almost new and did I realise the cost of a new one? Then the message was sent to the company. For the next four days, the messages went back and forward, regarding the carelessness of the crew, the poor supervision of the Chief Officer and the fact that we were trying to bankrupt the company. Eventually permission was granted and a new kettle finally arrived in Singapore. It was the cheapest possible piece of rubbish and it broke three weeks later. No power on earth could persuade the Captain to send another message to the company. The Bosun bought one in the end, which I told him on his leaving was quite generous. He told me not so; he had sold an old wire to pay for it and made a handsome profit!

If you have the budget, get a list of stores required so that they can be sent to different chandlers for the best prices.

28.4 Port Work

You might be allowed to paint overside in the port, but if you want to do this you need to ask the port if it is allowed.

You may also need consent for boats to be lowered and sent away, for a painting raft or for any repairs.

28.5 Medical

Although this is not necessarily your direct responsibility, it is within the sphere of your department. So ensure that if anyone needs a doctor or dentist that this is advised prior to thc ship's arrival.

28.6 Official Visitors

Try to obtain a list of officials or other visitors who intend boarding the ship during the port stay. Sometimes the agent can obtain this information and you might even get a chance of scheduling these visitors.

28.7 Fresh Water and Garbage

Fresh water is rarely a problem, except for the lengths of hose sometimes required to reach from the water mains to the ship's tanks. State how much you want and ask the pumping rate. This will give you an idea as to how long it will take.

Garbage is more of a problem. In theory, the port should provide garbage disposal bins at each berth so that the existing garbage can be dumped, with the ship continuing to place garbage in these until departure. In practice, this is rarely the case. There is often no garbage bin and service to take the garbage away must be paid for, with the costs so high that the operators refuse to pay, with the result that the ship sails away with garbage still onboard. All you can do is state that you require garbage disposal facilities.

29 Ballast Water Management

Ballast water management plans and forms are now part of the ship's port entry documentation. However, as ballast water management is still a relatively new imposition on ships and their personnel, I thought it appropriate to quote a few of the relevant parts of the IMO Resolution A.868(20) that will affect you.

8.1.1 Where a port State authority requires that specific ballast water procedures and/ or treatment option(s) be undertaken, and due to weather, sea conditions or operational impracticability such action cannot be taken, the master should report this fact to the port State authority as soon as possible and, where appropriate, prior to entering seas under its jurisdiction.

This is most relevant in a situation where a port requires a ship to be completely deballasted and, by doing this, the ship cannot be handled properly in a seaway. It is also relevant where a port requires the same and then expects the ship to anchor in winter conditions or in areas where high winds are prevalent.

9.1.2 Removing ballast sediment on a timely basis
Where practicable, routine cleaning of the ballast tank to remove sediments should be carried out in mid-ocean or under controlled arrangements in port or dry dock, in accordance with the provisions of the ship's ballast water management plan.

9.1.3 Avoiding unnecessary discharge of ballast water
If it is necessary to take on and discharge ballast water in the same port to facilitate safe cargo operations, care should be taken to avoid unnecessary discharge of ballast water that has been taken up in another port.

Notice the wording, 'where practicable'. Who decides this, the ship? And if the ship does, will the port accept the ship's decision?

9.2.1 Ballast water exchange

Near-coastal (including port and estuarine) organisms released in mid-ocean, and oceanic organisms released in coastal waters, do not generally survive.

When exchanging ballast at sea, guidance on safety aspects of ballast water exchange as set out in appendix 2 should be taken into account. Furthermore, the following practices are recommended:

- *where practicable, ships should conduct ballast exchange in deep water, in open ocean and as far as possible from shore. Where this is not possible, requirements developed within regional agreements may be in operation, particularly in areas within 200 nautical miles from shore. Consistent with 9.1.2 above, all of the ballast water should be discharged until suction is lost, and stripping pumps or eductors should be used if possible;*
- *where the flow-through method is employed in open ocean by pumping ballast water into the tank or hold and allowing the water to overflow, at least three times the tank volume should be pumped through the tank;*
- *where neither form of open ocean exchange is practicable, ballast exchange may be accepted by the port State in designated areas; and*
- *other ballast exchange options approved by the port State.*

It would seem that, on the majority of bulk carriers and tankers, owing to the stress problems, the exchange method is the one most favoured.

9.2.2 Non-release or minimal release of ballast water
In cases where ballast exchange or other treatment options are not possible, ballast water may be retained in tanks or holds. Should this not be possible, the ship should only discharge the minimum essential amount of ballast water in accordance with port States' contingency strategies.

This is recognition that, at times, it may not be possible to discharge the ballast water or part of it owing to weather, stability or stress on the structure, and the following supports that case:

11.3 In all cases, a port State authority should consider the overall effect of ballast water and sediment discharge procedures on the safety of ships and those onboard. Guidelines will be ineffective if compliance is dependent upon the acceptance of operational measures that put a ship or its crew at risk. Port States should not require any action of the master which imperils the lives of seafarers or the safety of the ship.

If there is a good reason why the discharge procedures have not been followed, you will undoubtedly be requested to prove your case. Logbook records of the weather conditions and your stability calculations will all be necessary to support your actions. Ensure that the Master is fully conversant with these prior to any examination and that he has concurred with your calculations.

The final two are worth noting:

11.10 *When sampling for research or compliance monitoring, the port State authority should give as much notice as possible to the ship that sampling will occur, to assist in planning staffing and operational resources.*

11.11 *The master has a general obligation to provide reasonable assistance for the above monitoring which may include provision of officers or crew, provision of the ship's plans, records pertaining to ballast arrangements and details concerning the location of sampling points.*

Owing to the involvement of laws now dealing with ballasting, you must discuss your intentions with the Master and keep him advised throughout of the situation. After all, he is the one who will be led off to jail!

30 Anchor Work

30.1 Maintenance

Although the anchor is a sturdy bit of kit, there are certain precautions that should be taken to ensure the correct functioning.

When heaving up the anchor, ensure that it is washed down properly, freeing the ground soil and debris from around the flukes and fluke swivel areas. If this is left, the debris can quickly build up and solidify, reducing the fluke angle and the efficiency of the anchor. It also reduces the build-up of mud in the chain locker and helps keep the suctions free. When chain has not been properly washed down, it can easily be seen by the flying dried mud that is thrown around the foc'sle when the anchor is next let go. Here is another point to think about. A large lump of dried mud can be rock hard. If this hits one of the foc'sle party, especially in the face, severe injuries could result.

If the ship is of the size and trade where breaking the anchor for buoy moorings might occur, it is wise to break the joining shackle at periodic intervals to ensure that it is not seized.

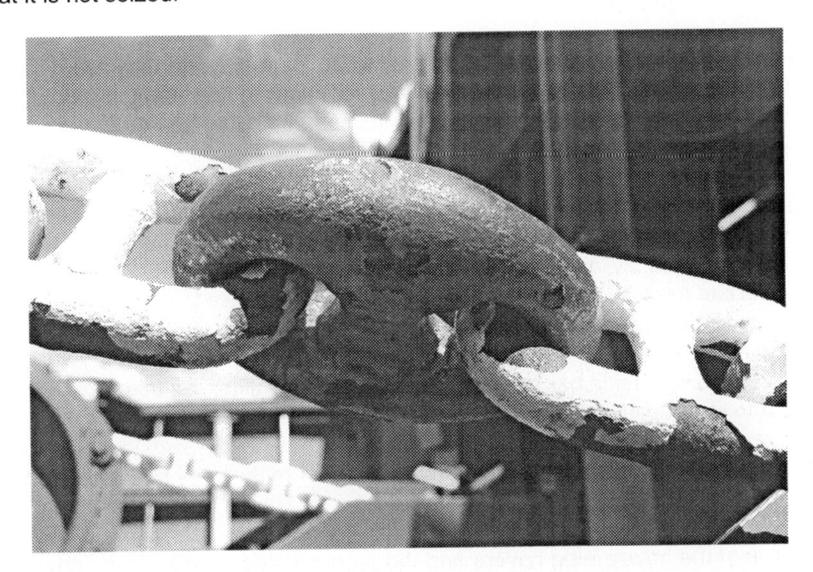

Once, as Chief Officer, having spent two days on an old 'type 14' general cargo ship, trying to break first one cable then the other ready for mooring in Hong Kong, I learnt the hard way. In the end, we cut through with burning gear. It turned out that the ship, which was 10 years old, had never had the Kenter joining shackles or any other broken, even in dry dock.

Occasionally, particularly after an anchorage when strain might have been put on the anchor, have the anchor walked out and view it from the jetty, looking for any sign of a bent shank or fluke. Check the main pin on the D anchor joining shackle. See that the split pin is in position and replace this if it is worn or missing. The main pin on the joining shackle can be spot welded to prevent loss.

Wire markings are used to assist with recognition of the number of shackles. This has been neglected on many ships but, when the cable is dirty or painting has been neglected, the wire marking can still be useful. The marking should be as follows:

At 15 fathoms: One turn of wire on the first stud from each side of the joining shackle

at 30 fathoms: Two turns of wire on the second stud from each side of the joining shackle at 45 fathoms: Three turns of wire on the third stud from each side of the joining shackle.

Then a similar pattern for further shackles.

Ensure that the cables are marked in clear white paint and that they are repainted regularly. This is still the best way for knowing how many shackles are out. The best way for this is to have white paint standing by for marking each time you heave your anchor.

Regular greasing of the windlass and removal of old grease, particularly from the brake spindle, ensures that the brake can be fully screwed up. This should be carried out frequently, especially on heavy bulk cargo vessels where the build-up of debris can mix with the grease and form a hard substance that can prevent the brakes from being properly applied.

Check the compression bar for wear, particularly at the sides, as this might enable the bar to slide up from the chain.

Have the chain stoppers greased regularly and ensure that they can be tightened fully.

Check that the hawse pipe covers and the spurling pipe covers fit properly and that, whether cement or foam is used for the spurling pipe, it is effective in stopping water ingress. Make sure that old cement and foam are removed from the spurling pipe.

Ensure that your stock of groundwork equipment is adequate for the tasks expected. The spare joining shackles, D rings and links should all be kept well greased and the spile pins ready. The wire strop for hanging off the anchor should be of the safe working load for the anchor and the stenhouse slip should be in good condition.

30.2 Anchor Procedures

Regardless of the fact that you should be on the bridge honing your skills for command, you could well find yourself stationed forward for anchoring. While all the orders will emanate from the bridge, always remember that they cannot see what is going on under the bow and, at night, can see very little of the foc'sle. It therefore remains for you to keep the bridge informed, with the appropriate reports, and oversee the safe anchoring or heaving up of the anchor.

Prior to arrival at the anchorage, it is good procedure to clear away the anchors. There are two reasons for this, one is that the ship will be entering coastal waters before anchoring and it is good seamanship to have your anchors cleared in coastal waters, and the other is that it gives you time to clear the anchors properly and ensure that everything is in order.

If you are anchoring at night, check that the lights are working and cleared of any covers if coming in from a long sea passage. Always clear away both anchors.

In deep water or on large vessels with heavy anchors, it is wise to walk the anchors back to just above the water. Then the Master can decide whether he wishes to walk them back all the way to the bottom or let them go from this position.

If letting the anchor run, make sure that no one is standing in front of the anchor cable. Don't forget to report the anchors ready for letting go and, when in the anchor position, check that all is clear for letting go, again advising the bridge.

Communications must be clear during anchoring.

30.3 Walking out the Anchor

This procedure is acceptable but certain precautions have to be taken. The vessel must not be drifting with a higher speed over the ground than the payout speed of the motor of the windlass (approx 0.1 knot). Due to the big gear ratio in the anchor windlass, a drifting speed higher than the payout speed will easily cause an over-speeding overload of the windlass motor and damage the motor, ie the vessel will be pulling the chain out. The chain stopper has to be engaged before the chain is tensioned. The chain stopper is the only element designed to arrest the vessel's movements. The anchor windlass motor must never be connected when the chain is under tension. If the chain is under tension, the main engine has to be used to slacken it before connection to the winch. A golden rule for all anchor and mooring equipment is that both the cable lifter unit and the mooring drums must always be kept disconnected from the motor while under tension. Before connecting a tensioned chain or a mooring line, the tension must be reduced below the nominal pull of the unit.

It is impossible to control a ship to a speed of 0.1 knots for periods of up to one hour, so walking back the anchor the whole way is not an option unless in very calm waters with little or no current as this will put severe strain on the windlass that it is not designed to take.

Once the chain is paid out it must not be held on the brake. Instead the stoppers must be put on and the cable slacked back until the weight of the cable is held on them as they are designed for this purpose.

The bridge is totally reliant on you telling them the direction of the cable and the weight on it and this should be constantly reported during the anchoring procedure.

30.4 Heaving Anchor

When heaving anchor, the cable should not be straining against the windlass. Instead the engines should be used to take the strain off the cable while heaving. Once again, the bridge is waiting for you to advise them of any strain on the cable and the direction the cable is leading.

Ensure that, as the cable comes in, the shackle number is passed to the bridge and that you repaint these shackles with white paint for future identification.

When the anchor is coming to the surface of the water, check that it is clear and, if so, report this. At night, you must have a bright beam light to shine on the anchor.

When the anchor is up and stowed you can put the brake and stoppers on and take it out of gear. If the Master requires, the anchors can then be secured for sea.

In all anchor operations there is an element of danger, so injuries happen every year. You should, therefore, be purely in a supervisory position and not driving the windlass or doing other work.

31 Port Arrival

For the last part of the port approach it is normal procedure for the Chief Officer to join the bridge team, unless the ship is to proceed on a prolonged river passage with you having to then go onto the bridge for watchkeeping. Your addition to the bridge in a busy port area, particularly at night, could considerably assist the Master in the navigation of the vessel.

31.1 Pilot Embarkation and Disembarkation

REQUIRED BOARDING ARRANGEMENTS FOR PILOT

In accordance with IMO requirements and IMPA recommendations

INTERNATIONAL MARITIME PILOTS' ASSOCIATION

H.Q.S 'Wellington', Temple Stairs, Victoria Embankment, London WC2R 2PN Tel: +44 20 7240 3973 Fax: +44 20 7240 3518

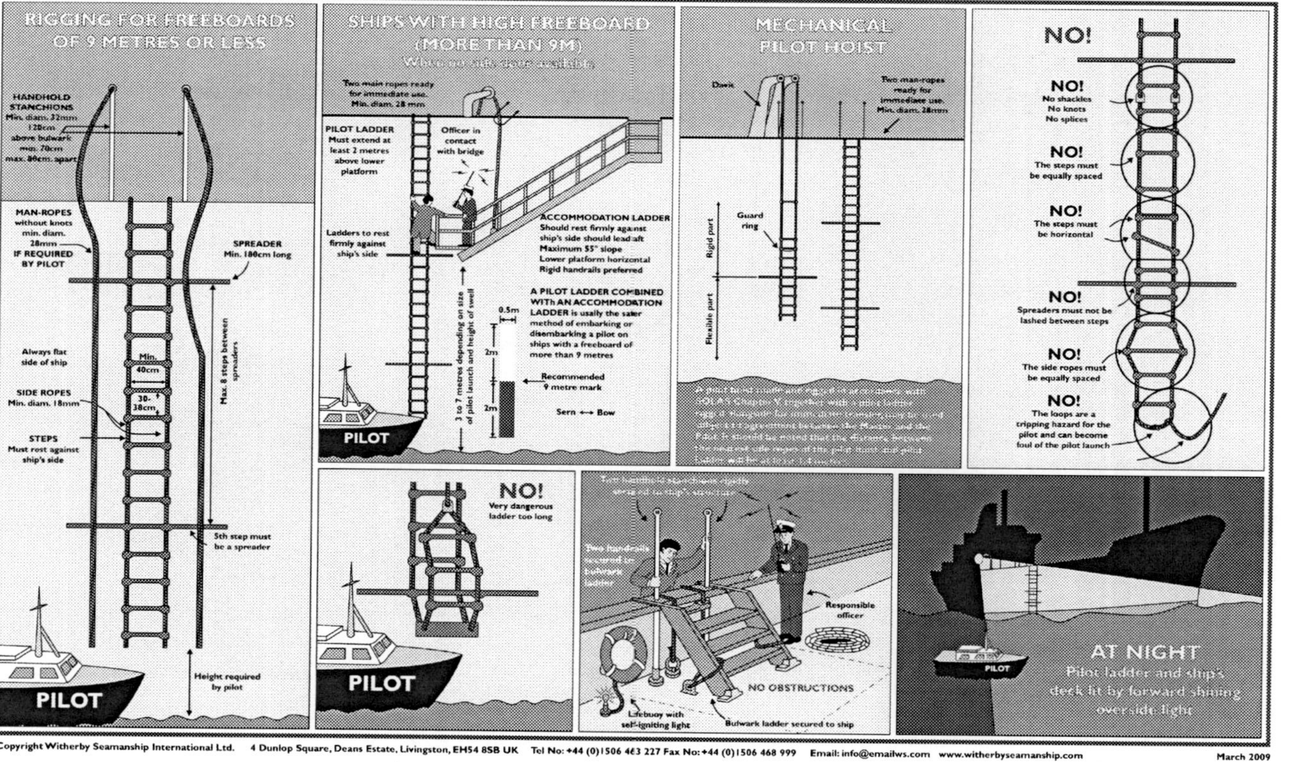

 4 Dunlop Square, Deans Estate, Livingston, EH54 8SB UK Tel No: +44 (0)1506 463 227 Fax No: +44 (0)1506 468 999 Email: info@emailws.com www.witherbyseamanship.com March 2009

The pilot ladder is of the utmost importance to the pilot. Whether the pilot embarkation point is through a gun port, directly by ladder to the main deck or by use of a combination ladder, it is essential that preparation is carried out in ample time. After preparation, the ladders must be physically tested and the area around them inspected by an officer. A pilot embarking and disembarking from a ship should be regarded as a potential hazard because of the use of ladders or a combination of ladders and gangways. Because this often occurs during a ship's voyage, or because the pilot does this so many times, it becomes a commonplace event rather than one where all parties involved maintain the utmost vigilance.

Proper inspection of pilot ladders is a neglected area. Too often a quick look over is given, rather than a full stretch out and inspection of each step and the lashings and seizing checked. A reasonable weight should be put on the ladder with a winch, and this should be carried out at least every four months.

Manropes should be inspected, even though they are not always required and some pilotage authorities consider them a nuisance as they get in the way when the ladder is used.

The illumination for the ladders should also be checked. The days where a cargo light dangles over the ladder on a length of rope with a 60 watt light bulb are over. It is also important that the side of the ship in the way of the ladder is also illuminated.

On most ships a lifebuoy is part of the standard equipment at the head of the pilot ladder, although this often is a decoration rather than an important tool of rescue. When the pilot boat comes alongside the ship has at least six knots way on. If the pilot falls into the sea a lifebuoy at the head of the ladder is of little use. It should be ready with a seafarer about twenty metres along the deck towards the stern. If the pilot falls the seafarer can throw the lifebuoy over the side and, if properly positioned, the pilot will be carried down to it by the speed of the ship through the water. Because of the difficulties that would be experienced by a person holding onto a lifebuoy that is being towed through the water at six knots it should not be secured to the ship. It should instead be regarded as an additional buoyancy aid that also assists with visual marking.

On large ships in ballast condition, the combination of an amidships gangway and ladder is used. When this type of system is in use preparation of the pilot ladder must include a check that the gangway and the ladder complement each other and that the ladder can be easily boarded from the gangway. It is essential that the pilot is escorted to the bottom of the gangway.

31.2 Deck Preparation

- Unrig the deck safety lines
- have the hatch top safety lines rigged

- check all the deck lighting
- check the decks for any sign of oil leaks
- if bunkering, ensure that the after scuppers are all sealed and allow for any oil spreading further up the deck
- check with the pilot if you can have the accommodation ladder swung out or whether there are any obstructions, such as cranes, that might be in the way
- have the mooring ropes flaked out and the heaving lines standing by.

Depending on the port, you might consider taking in your hoses and nozzles from the fireboxes and the lifebuoys.

31.3 Cargo Preparation

The port will want to start cargo immediately on arrival or, if it is the first port of call in a country, immediately after you are cleared by customs and immigration. You should have your holds, hatches and your ballasting ready.

You may be requested by the port to open hatches prior to arrival alongside. This is a common request in Australian and South African bulk ports. This you must strongly resist. It is a potentially dangerous practice and no port can insist on it. Your hatch top rails, chains and stoppers are not designed to have stress put on them when turning and listing.

31.4 Mooring

Problems with securing the vessel are commonly caused by a lack of crew to properly deal with all the moorings in the time required. On most ships there will be a tug fast forward and another tug aft, usually on the outboard side. Unless they are using their own lines, this takes away one of your mooring lines. You should have your remaining lines flaked out ready for paying out and the heaving lines fast on the forward line and on the spring. Have at least two heaving lines ready for use and see that the stoppers are in good order. At night, good lighting is essential.

Most pilots and Masters want a headline and a spring put out together forward and a stern line and a spring put out aft. This configuration in good weather is sensible, but you must have one man for driving the windlass and another to drive the winch for the spring line. Then you need at least two men on each line to pay them out. That takes four seafarers on each station. How many cargo ships have eight seafarers? The answer is that you are only able to safely put out one line at a time. In good weather, this is probably acceptable as the tugs can hold the ship in while the ship is being made fast, but what about in bad weather?

In bad weather, particularly if the wind is blowing the ship off the berth, the bridge will want the lines put out as soon as possible.

It is important that you notify the bridge of your ability as too often the situation deteriorates into the pilot shouting that the crew and officers are useless as he struggles to keep the ship from breaking away. If the anchor must be let go during this operation, it further adds to the pandemonium. One danger in letting go the anchor in an emergency is that the officer in charge on the foc'sle will forget to check over the side to see that it is clear of the tug and the tug's lines. Find out from the bridge which line is to have priority and then you can concentrate on getting it out. Any other line during this operation must be regarded as a bonus. It does help if the Master explains the crewing situation to the pilot on joining and then he can make a judgement on the weather and whether to delay the berthing.

You must remember that, for safety reasons, throughout this operation it is essential that the officers at their stations remain in a supervisory capacity. Only by standing back watching and directing the operation can you control it.

31.5 Watchkeeping

In port you are responsible for the watch list and anyone wanting to change it can do so only with your authority.

On most ships the normal system is for the Chief Officer to go onto daywork and the Second and Third Officers to have a system of 6 hours on and 6 hours off. No sensible Captain or Chief Officer will expect them to be on their feet all the time and so they will of necessity occasionally use the cargo office. This is perfectly acceptable provided that they are in touch with what is happening on the decks. There are different ways in which this can be done. If you have cadets there is no reason why they cannot oversee the decks, provided they have read and understood your cargo and standing orders. If the OOW is only absenting himself for a short time a duty rating can do the same, with both of these keeping in touch with the duty officer on the personal communication systems.

In the normal rush of things in port, for many there is often little time for anyone to think of going ashore. But there are times and ships where this is possible, particularly when weather or breakdowns interfere with normal operations. If you are on a ship where the opportunity for shore leave is rare and such an occasion occurs, do try to give as many as you can the chance to get ashore. This includes your officers and, if you are not going, consider standing the watch to allow them both to go.

31.6 Visitors

As Chief Officer you are not particularly bothered about the company's sensibilities regarding who is appropriate or not, just that they do not disturb the work of the ship. However, certain decorum must be observed. Remember that you are nominally the head of discipline onboard.

If the Captain has a policy, this must be followed. However, if it is a general one that says 'I don't like visitors' this leaves it open to you. What is important is that you know who is onboard the ship at all times, not just for security purposes, but also for safety.

A few suggested rules:

- All visitors onboard must have permission, whether this is from the Captain, you or the Chief Engineer
- they must, on boarding, sign an indemnity to protect the company
- they should remain at all times with the person who invited them and that person must be responsible for their behaviour
- everyone onboard must understand that any visitor can be requested to leave at any time
- under no circumstances should they be allowed in working areas of the ship, except with the explicit permission of the Master
- should they visit working areas, they must wear the appropriate PPE
- finally, it might be worthwhile printing some visitor passes if your company does not provide them. They need the ship's name and official stamp, a space for the visitor's name and the name and rank or rating of the crew member visited, date and time, port and signature of the head of department.

This is suggested because visitors are often refused entry to the berth without the authority of the ship and, when this occurs, you generally are the one pestered for a pass at a busy time.

In most cases the person being visited will have to attend the berth entrance and escort the visitor to the ship. This is sensible.

31.7 Security

The ISPS Code is now in force and your ship is obliged to follow it. The degree to which you do this often depends on the crew you have available. Since its introduction, no maritime administration has required a company to increase the manning so no company has done so, which can cause you a problem. For example, how a ship with two officers, an engineer and two seafarers can maintain a gangway security watch is beyond any reasonable answer.

However, you could be with an enlightened company that provides CCTV cameras or employs a shore security service, although such companies are very few and far between.

The rules state that the ports must provide:

- Port facility security plans
- port facility security officers.

In addition, the requirements for both ports and ships are:

- Monitoring and controlling access
- monitoring the activity of peoples and cargo
- ensuring that the security communications are readily available.

I would have thought that if the port is providing the security required by the regulations it could be treated as a secure area. If that is the case, and the ship is in a secure area, why are we also required to provide additional security? Obviously there are ports and ships where common sense dictates that such additional security must be maintained, but the blanket rule does take away informed assessment.

31.8 Gangway Watch

If the gangway watch is to be maintained then practical rules for the gangway must be enforced. The following is a suggestion of what you could include if they are not already dictated by the company security officer:

- All entry/exit to the vessel must be via the gangway
- the gangway security notice must be posted on the gangway
- the gangway watch must be kept during working hours
- the gangway watch will be relieved on the gangway
- all visitors to the vessel must be recorded on the visitors' form provided
- new joining crew are to be checked against the company list
- visitors are also to be checked against the company-provided list of contractors
- visitors without any ID are not to be allowed onboard until the OOW or the Master have been informed
- all visitors to the vessel are liable to be searched. 5% *must* be searched
- suspicious packages must not to be allowed into the vessel. If they are required to be opened, the carrier is to open them.

Any questions should be directed to the OOW or to the ship security officer.

31.9 People you do not want to see

The local evangelists

When you arrive in some ports, the word is out that you have a mixed crew of different and indifferent faiths. This can attract evangelists like bees to the honey pot in an effort to see that all recognise the 'true faith', whatever that may be. It has always impressed me the way in which the crews receive them with courtesy and listen to their words, possibly because they have a car and will take them to the local supermarket before a quick stop at the place of worship!

The Coastguard and Port State Control

Notice the incorrectly rigged safety net

While they may feel like a real nuisance when you are up to your eyeballs in work, they have a job to do and overall the ships and the sea are better off with them than without them. Therefore, as seafarers, we must accept the need for their inspections and assist them as much as possible. They board many ships and can tell whether it is being run properly within a few minutes onboard. If they see your ship as well run their stay will be short and friendly. Naturally they head for the Captain's cabin, everyone does, and he then passes them to you. Pass them on to the Second or Third Mate as there is no golden rule that says they have to be dealt with by a senior officer.

Be careful that you have everything in order, particularly the paperwork. On many ships the Master will deal with this side of things but, as the coastguard can appear at any time and the Master could be ashore, it is best that on arrival at any port the papers and documents are available on the bridge, under lock and key.

31.10 People you do want to see

Apart from your agent, there is the local chaplain from the Seafarers' Club. I should not have to tell you how important this man is in countless ports in dealing with the many problems that can arise with personnel. The improvement to morale and welfare they make to seafarers' lives onboard, and their assistance in providing an opportunity to get off the ship when possible, make them the most welcome visitor to any ship. Always ensure you have time to meet these men as, regardless of religious differences, their one concern is the welfare of those onboard.

32 The Gangway

The Gangways, regardless of the size of ship, is a constant source of problems. On small vessels, it often has to be moved to different deck levels with the rise and fall of the tide. Any move of the gangway includes a move of the safety netting and the gangway platform at the inboard end, particularly if it is hooked onto the top of a rail.

On larger vessels with a fixed system and a swivel platform, the rollers can often cope with the rise and fall, allowing the gangway freedom to move along the jetty provided there are no obstacles in the way. The problem here is that many jetties, in their initial construction, had the crane tracks built too close to the edge, with the result that there is little room between the cranes and the ship's side. This often means that, when the cranes need to move past the gangway, it must be hoisted in to avoid damage. This particularly applies to very large ships with amidships gangways. With the movement of shore equipment and often the proximity of bollards, it is essential that the gangway is tended.

In rivers or berths where there is large vessel traffic past your ship, regardless of the speed regulations or the care that pilots and Masters take, there will always be some movement caused by passing vessels. This can be alleviated by ensuring that lines are tight. It is wise to consider hoisting your gangway a few feet above the ground rather than risking possible damage to the rollers.

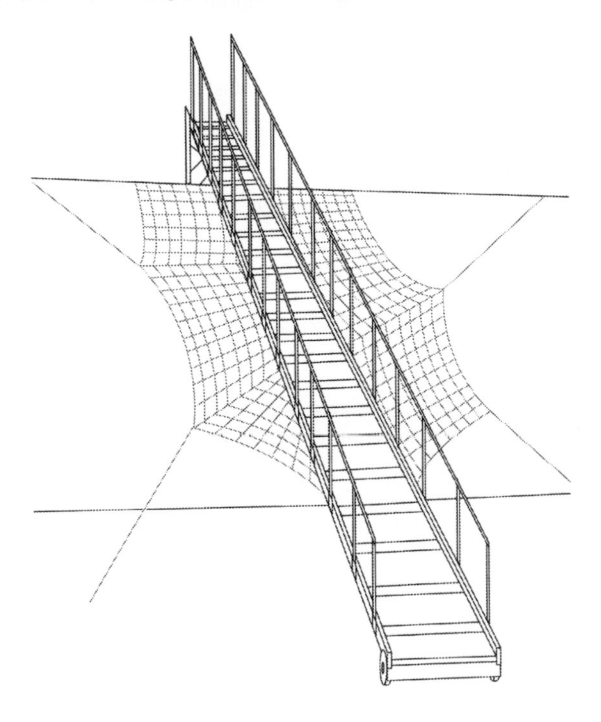

Remember that the safety net MUST go from the ship to the shore, and not just be wrapped around the gangway where it does no good at all. If there are no bollards or eye rings where the ends can be secured on the shore, then two oil drums can be filled with cement, eyes put in the top and these can be used in any port as required.

A major problem on large vessels is where an amidships gangway is in use. Being amidships it can be out of sight and out of mind, so you must ensure that the duty officer is keeping a regular watch on it. Next problem is cargo debris dropping on those using it. This has been a major issue for years and countless Chief Officers and Masters on countless ships have requested gangway sheltering to be provided as part of the equipment. Very rarely has any company supplied it. This can often be a dangerous situation, particularly for those boarding. I suggest that you have a notice made or added to the existing ones at the head and foot of the gangway, warning of possible falling cargo debris.

32.1 Gangway Maintenance

Your gangway has an SWL and you must be careful that this is not exceeded, particularly when bringing heavy stores onboard.

Check that the stanchion holders are not broken or loose.

The rigging and steps must be tight and not slippery. They must be free from oil and grease and not loose.

The gangway must be well lit, either by an overhead light that must illuminate the entire gangway, or by a light string running along the gangway length.

One of the serious problems that can occur with a gangway is the cracking of the underside of the turntable and supports. As this is hidden, it is quite often not noticed. It is, therefore, essential that the gangway is lifted off the platform and examined.

The gangway falls and wires must be well greased and in good order with the wires in date.

The head of the gangway must be clean, not just for safety but because this is the first impression that all visitors will get of your ship.

Make sure that the lower platform rollers are well greased and free running. Normally the platform should not be on the ground, but when you have to extend the gangway out beyond the vertical falls, this will occur. It is in this position that most gangway damage occurs.

When you have a gangway in this position, ensure that you have good holding lines attached to the bottom. In some ports, these will be pinched so ensure that there are lines provided just before letting go. This will enable the shore riggers to pay out slowly and allow the gangway to ease itself back to the vertical. If they just leave it, when you hoist it will drag sideways damaging the roller, or it will be out until clear of the ground and then let it go, causing it to swing in hard against the ship's side. Either way, you will get damage.

33 Port Responsibilities

Once upon a time, when you were a junior officer, you could actually think about arrival in port as a change of scenery, a heavier work load and the possibility of getting ashore and relaxing. Any breakdown that caused delays to cargo work or sailing was a bonus and looked forward to as a further chance to get ashore. Those days are over. It is in port that your problems and workload dramatically increase and where you really will earn your money.

The ship is now yours and you need to be in control.

For all practical purposes the ship is yours. While the Captain still has the responsibility and the final word, this is where you will demonstrate your management and command abilities. You will have two main concerns, the cargo and the ship, and you must plan for both. The Captain has his work cut out just dealing with the port officials and their paperwork, let alone the many other problems, and if the ship is on short port stays (of hours rather than days) there is a good chance you will not see him near the decks.

I have been on runs on the coast where, in some ports, the engine was left on standby and the tugs stayed alongside ready for leaving again. A few ports in succession like this can cause severe fatigue in all of you.

You must be able to depend on your officers to at least carry out your orders. It is essential that you have standing orders that are clear and concise but covering every eventuality. If your officers are inexperienced, they will still have clear guidelines to follow.

On two occasions, once in Gladstone and the other in Le Havre, I was ashore as Master when the weather changed without warning and the Chief Officer had to deal with the ship being blown off the berth. In both cases, I had a superb Chief Officer who ran the ship in port with an iron hand. There were no problems, the ports were notified, tugs called and gangways lifted, and when I returned in each case just logbook notes indicated what had happened. That man was a proper Chief Officer. On reflection, that is probably why I was ashore without too many concerns!

The following is an example of a Chief Officer's standing orders in port, which might provide you with a few ideas of what you could include in yours. You could be on a ship where the Master has his own and yours will supplement his, in which case many of the items here will have been covered. Do not depend on this though. If the Captain does not issue any then you must issue your own.

33.1 Chief Officer's Port Standing Orders

1. *The OOW will ensure that the ship is tight alongside and that the mooring lines are adjusted with the rise and fall of the ship.*
2. *In the event of the weather deteriorating, the OOW should not hesitate to order additional moorings to be put out to ensure the securing of the ship. If required, the outboard anchor may be walked out to the bottom. Should there be danger of the ship coming off the berth, the VHF should be used to contact the port and tugs ordered to keep the vessel alongside.*
3. *The OOW will ensure that the gangway is kept at the correct height to avoid damage, paying special attention to passing vessels. Ensure that the gangway is safe, well lit and secure at all times.*
4. *When ships are passing it is important to ensure that all the mooring lines are tight. Should any damage to the ship or lines occur during the passing of a vessel, the time and name of the ship should be immediately entered in the port log and the port authorities advised of the occurrence by the VHF. A damage report should then be filed.*
5. *Safety equipment is to be worn by all personnel, both ship and shore, when on the decks.*
6. *In the event of any oil spill, the ship's emergency response plan is to be followed.*
7. *It is important that any oil in the water near the ship is investigated immediately. The ER should be checked and any pumping that is taking place stopped until the source of the oil is established. If it is from the ship then order 6 applies and the harbour authorities are to be immediately advised. If it is not from the ship, the terminal operators are to be advised and the agents notified. An immediate entry is to be made in the port log together with the names of those notified.*

8. *Any deposits of oil or grease on the decks must be immediately cleared and the area secured until safe for use.*

9. *During the hours of darkness, all gangway and deck lights must be switched on and working.*

10. *Should an accident occur onboard it is imperative that, if required, shore assistance is obtained as soon as possible. If there is no immediate contact or telephone available, then the port authorities should be contacted on the VHF. The following information should be given:*

    a. *Name of ship.*

    b. *Position in the port.*

    c. *Nature of the problem and what services are required.*

    An officer should be stationed at the gangway to ensure that, on the arrival of the requested services, they can be immediately directed to the accident area.

11. *In the event of any injury to any person, shore or crew, it is essential that the facts of the accident are recorded as soon as possible. The following are required:*

    a. *Nature of injury.*

    b. *Treatment given if any.*

    c. *Place and time.*

    d. *Lighting conditions.*

    e. *Safety equipment worn by the injured person.*

    f. *Any suspicion of drug or alcohol use.*

    g. *Statements and names of witnesses.*

    h. *The company accident form is to be completed.*

12. *In the event of any damage occurring to the ship or equipment, a damage report is to be filed, signed by the required personnel and an entry made in the port log.*

13. *No shore worker is to enter the accommodation except on official business. Any shore worker found in the accommodation is to be challenged as to their presence and either conducted to the person they wish to see or requested to leave.*

14. *If at any time the OOW observes a shore worker behaving in an erratic manner, or suspects that they might be under the influence of alcohol or drugs, or that they are working in such a manner that they might cause injury or damage to others or to the ship, then their supervisor is to be informed. This is to be entered in the port log. Should their behaviour continue, the OOW is to request their removal from the ship.*

15. *Each morning, the deck area in the way of the gangway and accommodation entrance is to be washed down and the main deck alleyway cleaned.*
16. *Flags will be hoisted at 0800 and lowered at sunset.*
17. *The bridge equipment checklist is to be completed when testing gear prior to departure.*
18. *Prior to departure the bridge wings and coamings will be washed down and the bridge windows cleaned.*
19. *Should the OOW have difficulties at any time, if any accident occurs, or there are difficulties with shore personnel, he must consult his head of department and the Chief Officer if onboard. The Chief Officer is to be advised immediately of any accident, damage or pollution incident. In dealing with any member of the ship's company or shore personnel, the OOW is acting on the Chief Officer's behalf and with his authority and, provided that he has acted in a responsible manner, will always have his support. All visitors to the ship are to be dealt with in a courteous manner regardless of who or what they are.*
20. *The gangway board must state clearly the date and time of departure and the time the crew must be onboard. This must be put on the board at least 24 hours prior to the ship's ETD.*
21. *'No smoking' signs are to be displayed and enforced where relevant.*
22. *No alcohol is to be brought onto the ship by any crew member or shore worker.*
23. *During bunkering, the pollution equipment will be placed out on deck at the bunkering position ready for immediate use and the appropriate signal is to be hoisted. The bunkering checklist MUST be completed prior to bunkering operations.*
24. *The Ship Security Plan is to be complied with depending on the Security State the vessel is at. Normally this will be State 1. Any persons onboard who are not identified as bona fide workers are to be challenged and identified.*
25. *The OOW will obtain, each morning in port, the weather forecast and bring any change in the weather conditions to the attention of the Chief Officer and the Master.*
26. *The draught will be taken at least once per watch.*

33.2 Shifting Ship

The shifting of the ship in port, if it is a dead ship move, is your job not the Captain's, although if you are new he might well take interest! You do not have to go on the bridge for this and two officers, one forward and one aft, can easily take care of this with communications between each other. Keep a watch on the wind though and if you consider that the weather is not conducive to a simple shift do not make the move. Remember that any shift is for the port at their request. You can always request a tug to standby at their expense or even a pilot if you feel that one is required.

One more point, you are not always at instant readiness to shift ship nor should you be. The port has to give you ample notice to their request for a shift for you to ensure that you have sufficient crew onboard. If they do not they have no right to demand an instant shift and you are perfectly justified to require time to prepare or even wait for crew to return. Do not try to do this if you are short of crew.

33.3 Garbage Disposal

£40,000 fine for ship caught dumping a plastic bag at sea

THE MASTER and the owners of a chemical tanker have been fined a total of A$97,500 (just over £40,000) by a court in Australia for dumping a plastic bag in the

ucts found aboard the Bow De Jin during an inspection in December 2002.

Each bag was sealed with a numbered plastic tie, which was

The regulations regarding this should be posted in the galley and the bridge and everyone these days is fairly conversant with the procedures. In most cases, I have observed that most seafarers do follow them quite willingly, seeing the sense and reason for them. There will always be the odd one though who unthinkingly heaves something over the side.

The problem is that, over any prolonged period and no matter what you incinerate, there is a build-up of garbage, particularly when ships are on the coasts for prolonged periods. To cope with this ports are supposed to provide a garbage removal service. The majority of well managed ports do, although on occasion their service is capable of breakdown by running out of skips, lack of personnel or the inevitable 'it's the weekend' syndrome. Unfortunately, there are too many ports still with little interest in assisting ships and in such cases the only garbage removal is either by private contractors or by leaving it onboard.

34 Pollution

It is almost obligatory to mention pollution when discussing anything to do with ships, and there is enough emotion left to stir the hearts of the media whenever an incident occurs. Ships these days have the best record of pollution care but that is regrettably not recognised, with the slightest incident being enough to have the local politicians storming onto the stage and the Captains dragged off to prison. All of this is regardless of the IMO regulations regarding treatment of the ships and their crew.

When the ship is coming alongside, keep a good eye out for oil on the water in way of the ship and, if there is any spotted, draw the attention of the Captain to it and enter it in your logbook. It is interesting to note the disinterest shown by the ports when it is their pollution but the alacrity with which they respond if they think that it is yours.

Accidental pollution seems to come from machinery both ashore and afloat rather than bunkering operations, over which great care is now taken. This doesn't mean you can relax in ensuring that all the precautions are taken, so block the scuppers and ensure that the oil pollution prevention equipment is ready standing by and that the crew are trained to use it. Crew and officers must keep a continuous watch on all deck machinery where, without warning, a hydraulic pipe can burst or leak. Everyone must know where to shut the oil off and shut down the motors.

It is wise to have mats and a sack of sawdust standing by at strategic locations. On bulk carriers this would mean near each hatch, ready for instant use. When any accident happens it is often no one's fault, but the more you can show that you did all you could to avoid any oil going into the water, the better it will be.

34.1 Bunkering

Bunkering requires that you coordinate with the bunkering officer as to his requirements for pollution control. Bunkering is a responsibility of the engineering department. However, pollution control is everyone's responsibility as, apart from pollution, it is in the ship's interest that any required assistance is given by departments to each other.

When bunkering in poor weather, it is essential that a good watch is kept on the moorings of the ship and, if bunkering from a barge, of the barge as well. A duty engineer should be on deck monitoring the operations. You will also have to ensure that a close check is maintained on the deck scuppers and that these are drained off regularly to avoid any build-up of rainwater.

Remember that if any pollution does occur, you must call the appropriate authorities immediately and then, when questioned, say nothing until your P&I representative attends.

35 Surveys

Much of the ship's time seems to be taken up with inspections and surveys of some type or another. Surveys are a part of our life in port and they must be taken in your stride. Some are essential, such as cargo and P&I, while others such as the standard classification surveys have a time window.

I am pleased to say that there is a growing realisation of the problems facing ships with constraints on time and manning. With this realisation have begun efforts to endeavour, where possible, to schedule the visits.

With all surveys it helps to ensure that any required documentation is ready for viewing and inspection. In addition, if you know any areas of the ship that are going to be surveyed, these can be prepared by having tanks opened and vented ready for entry and hatches battened down ready for hose testing.

Over the years, I learnt a great deal from listening and working with surveyors and rarely did I have any problems, except the standard ones of time and work pressures. If you meet them with a friendly professional approach in most cases this will be reciprocated and the survey will go better and be over faster, which is what everyone wants. By all means ask questions when you do not understand something; don't be worried about displaying any lack of knowledge, this is part of your learning process.

36 Cargo Operations

The primary reason for the ship being in port is for the discharge and loading of cargo. Once again, you cannot be there all the time, although many try. You must rely on your officers during the times you are asleep and for that you must give them specific cargo orders relating directly to the cargo you are loading or discharging at that specific port. If you do not do this you will constantly be called out on quite trivial matters.

36.1 The Cargo Log and your Daily Instructions

I suggest that each time you write these you put them in the front of the cargo logbook. The following are some suggestions that you might like to include:

- How you want the cargo stowed or loaded
- lashing and dunnaging if a dry cargo
- the cargo plan
- the recording of damage to cargo
- the ballasting programme
- the topping off of tanks
- the soundings or ullages
- overboard discharge
- stoppages
- when to be called
- the handover
- cargo disputes.

There are others but this will provide a starting position.

In your cargo office should be a list of tidal ranges for the duration of the ship's stay, the contact numbers of all the port emergency services, a watch list for officers and ratings and, for each day, a weather fax or similar to provide an update of the expected weather conditions.

It is a good idea to write up a cargo load and discharge record/reference book to be kept on the vessel so that subsequent Chief Officers will have something to refer to when it's their turn. Also, if you return to the vessel, you will have a good reference book to work from, which will make life a little easier. This book should have a copy of loading and discharging plans and comments as to how things worked in the various ports.

37 Cargo and Cargo Terms

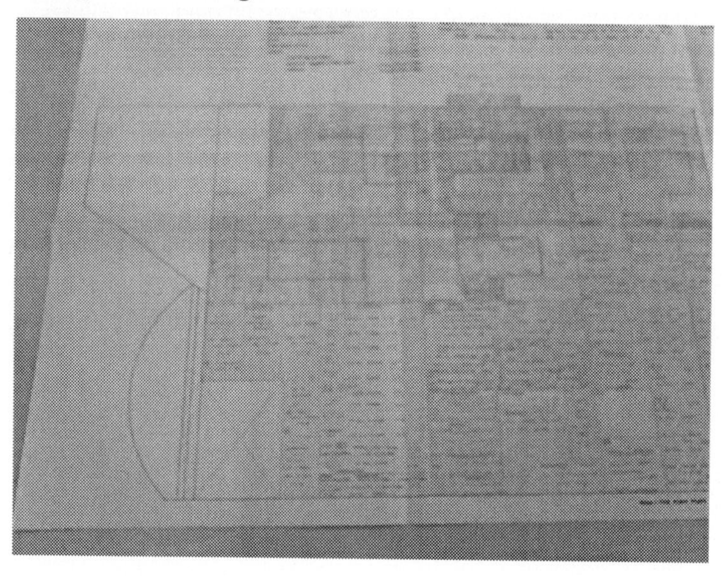

37.1 Mate's Receipt

This is the receipt, signed by the Mate of the ship responsible for cargo operations, for goods received onboard the ship. It should be identical to the Bill of Lading as the Bill of Lading is based on the Mate's Receipt.

It is now being replaced in many trades by the Standard Shipping Note.

This note or receipt should be endorsed with notes on the condition of the cargo, such as rust stained, pitting, broken bags, etc. In addition, when there is a dispute in the quantity, the lower figure of the tally should be used with the number in dispute stated.

37.2 Bill of Lading (B/L)

Although the B/L is the responsibility of the Master, it is such an important document that you should know about it and what it is for.

The B/L is a document of title giving the holder 'right of possession'. It is evidence that the holder of the original document is the rightful owner of the goods.

This is a receipt for goods that have been loaded into the vessel. It is a document of title to the goods and a contract governing the receipt, carriage and delivery of the goods.

The reason why there is such dispute over any endorsement of the B/L is that 'clean' B/Ls as opposed to 'dirty' B/Ls are required by the banks as a condition of issue of a Letter of Credit (LoC), the issue of which is a requirement for early payment to the exporter by the bank.

37.3 Deadfreight

This is a claim made that the ship is not loaded to her full capacity, ie 'her marks', by the charterer against the operator, although there can be a claim the other way. Examples of this claim would be on the basis that the ship did not load to her allowable marks or that too much ballast or bunkers were carried, both of which, if correct, would limit the amount of cargo being carried.

37.4 Laytime

This is the period of time allowed for loading and discharging. A charter party may also be claused to provide separate laytime for discharge and loading.

37.5 Demurrage

This is the money payable to the owner for delay in loading and/or discharging after the laytime has expired, for which the owner is not responsible.

37.6 Notice of Readiness (NoR)

This is tendered by the Master on the ship's arrival within the port limits. It is the notice to the charterer, shipper, receiver or other person as required by the charter that the ship has arrived at the port or berth and is ready to load/discharge. In most charter parties the date of acceptance of an NoR is the date and time for the commencement of the laydays.

It is most important that this notice is tendered immediately on the arrival of the ship, usually to the agent who will then ensure delivery to the charterer or the charterer's agent unless the agent is acting for both parties. In many cases the tendering of this notice is required during office hours so there is reason for urgency in delivery as a few minutes' delay can translate into a day's delay or, in the case of a weekend, a wait until the Monday morning.

37.7 On-Hire, Off-Hire

On-hire/off-hire surveys are usually carried out by independent surveyors with the owner and charterer paying an equal cost for such survey. The on-hire survey will state the bunkers onboard (ROB), the general condition of the ship, the state of the holds or tanks and their suitability for the intended cargoes, and any existing damage in these cargo spaces. Once this is completed a delivery certificate will be issued, which should be attached to the on-hire survey report.

The off-hire is similar, carried out at a time and place of re-delivery specified in the charter party. The charterer must deliver the vessel in 'the same good order as when delivered to the charterer, fair wear and tear excepted'.

A re-delivery certificate will be issued. Any repairs required to make good any damage can be carried out either prior to or after the re-delivery survey, or may wait until a suitable port or dry docking according to the agreed charter party clauses.

The charterer may be allowed to deliver the vessel 'dirty' and an agreed sum will be paid as compensation for damages.

Off-hire can also occur during the period of the charter for a number of reasons and a charter party will normally contain clauses to this effect, relating to the dry docking of the ship or relating to breakdown of the ship or cargo equipment, damage or accidents, in fact anything that prevents the normal operation of the ship to the charterer's requirements. In such an event the charterer is not required to pay hire money for the duration of the breakdown. This off-hire can be specified as starting after a certain period and, on busy liner trades, it is not unusual to have the off-hire starting within a very short period. When ships are on such tight off-hire clauses, it is important that they maintain a running record of the 'downtime' onboard and what the downtime relates to. A blackout will affect the whole ship and, if using ship's cargo gear, stop all operations, but a breakdown of only one crane or gantry will affect only a percentage of the cargo handling capacity.

At the end of the cargo operations, the ship's tally and that of the shore operations should agree.

Think of off-hire as having to fulfil three basic conditions:

- There must be a loss of time to the charterer
- the loss of time is caused by an event which falls within the named clauses in the charter party
- it has the effect of preventing the full working of the vessel.

37.8 Cargo Stowage

Although the charter party, if carried, is generally seen as within the Master's sphere of responsibility, there are a number of clauses that have a bearing on your job as the cargo officer. It would be wise to ask the Master if you may read the charter party or if there are any clauses of which you should be aware, such as off-hire times, stowage and lashing responsibilities.

The charter party should be checked for clauses regarding responsibility for stowage. It is often all in the wording.

In the Canadian Transport Company v Court Line Ltd (1940) it was stated:

> *The supervision of the stowage by the Captain is a matter of course, he has to in any event protect his ship from being made unseaworthy; and in other respects he no doubt has the right to interfere if he considers that the proposed stowage might impose a liability upon his owners. If it could be proved by the charterers that the bad stowage was caused only by the Captain's orders and that their own proposed stowage would have caused no damage, that might enable them to escape liability.*

Referring to the phrase 'the supervision of the stowage by the Captain', these words expressly give the Master the right, which I think he must have in any case, to supervise the operations of the charterer in loading and stowing. To the extent that the Master exercises supervision and limits the charterer's control over the stowage, the charterer's liabilities will be limited to the same degree.

If the charter party states 'supervision' and the Master limits himself to protecting the ship from damage and ensuring the seaworthiness of his vessel, the charterer will be liable for any damage to the cargo.

I loaded a deck cargo of timber in Northern Canada for transportation to Europe. The ship was not a timber vessel and the cargo was loaded high with only chains securing the stow. I pointed out the inadequacy of this stowage to the charterer to no avail and, after discussions with my operator and because the ship would still be seaworthy, we sailed. In the Gulf of Mexico, the ship encountered a storm and rolled heavily, with the resultant breaking of the chains and loss over the side of a good proportion of the cargo. On arrival at Cristobal the cargo had to be restowed. All the loss and time delays were to the charterer's account as the charter party stated 'supervision'. I had also issued a letter of protest to the charterer holding them responsible for any damages to the ship.

If the word 'responsibility' is inserted in the charter party then the ship is responsible not only for damage to the cargo but also to the ship.

37.9 Stevedore Damage

Stevedore damage on many ships is a way of life, especially at discharge ports on bulk carriers. The damage caused by heavy grabs not only damages the hold but further impacts on the steelwork in the tanks beneath and to the side of the holds.

Damage by shore labour on any ship must be instantly recorded and reported to the senior shore representative onboard, usually a foreman. In addition, the Captain must be advised as he will have to write a letter of protest regarding the matter. Small damage that occurs is usually settled on the spot, with the stevedores calling in repair personnel to make good the damage.

For more serious damage that cannot be repaired in the port, a damage report must be filed with copies to the stevedores and agent. Responsibility will be decided on by the operators and the charterers on the basis of your report. Should the stevedores refuse to sign, note this in the place of their signature.

Most stevedores, not surprisingly, do not report damage unless it is to their own equipment and in their opinion caused by the ship. You should never admit your responsibility even if it is blatantly obvious. It is essential that during cargo operations you and your officers take time to examine the working areas for any signs of damage. This applies particularly to hatch coamings and rails in way of the cargo working and, of course, the holds themselves.

37.10 Stopping the Cargo Operations

In the chapter on heavy weather, I discussed the problems of stopping the cargo operations and the consequences. Regardless of this, there is one occasion when you are perfectly justified in stopping the operations and that is if the cargo plan is not being followed. This is very serious, particularly on ships that have critical stability problems. In such cases the cargo operations must be stopped immediately until the situation is resolved. You are entitled to take any action required to ensure the terminal's compliance.

38 Cargo Safety

38.1 General

No smoking on the deck of a tanker is obvious, but it applies to other ship types.

Whatever the ship, certain precautions are universal:

- Smoking. I am sure you know that all smoking on the decks in port, regardless of the cargo is banned. If you should find any shore labour ignoring this ruling, you should immediately advise the foreman and request the offender's removal from the ship. Remember this is your ship not theirs. If he fails to do this, issue a note of protest
- drink or drugs. If you suspect that any shore labour is under the influence of these then you must contact the foreman immediately and have them removed. If they are operating any equipment have the cargo operations stopped until their removal

Even shore staff must wear PPE.

- PPE. The appropriate PPE is required for all, whether crew or shore labour
- only properly authorised personnel are permitted near the cargo operational areas
- mooring lines must be properly tended as the ship rises and falls with the tide and with the change in draught due to the cargo operations
- the cargo area should be well lit and the decks free from oil and grease
- all the lighting should be operating properly
- the OOW and the duty watch must be identifiable and their whereabouts known to each other and to the shore supervisor.

38.2 Tankers

While all cargo operations require care and attention, tankers require a far higher degree of alertness during cargo operations owing to the speed of loading, the dangers of pollution by either oil or gas and the dangers to personnel that accidents can bring. A basic list of the most important points is as follows:

- The vessel's cargo control room must be manned at all times when cargo pumps are running during any cargo operation
- during connection of the manifold to the shore hard arm or hoses, no other cargo operations can take place, particularly those involving the operating of cargo pumps
- during cargo operations, good tanker practice must be maintained, such as keeping double valve segregation, where fitted, and shutting all valves that don't need to be open

- when lining up cargo systems a system of double-checking must be implemented
- safety features, such as cargo tank 98% high level alarms and interlocks, can only be overridden in exceptional circumstances and then great care must be taken to constantly monitor the situation.

If a ship's crew have any reservations with regard to the operational procedures adopted by a terminal or berth, such as lack of information, no direct communications with the terminal or poor supervision or coordination, the crew should make such reservations known to the terminal or berth operator and to the ship owner or operator. Operations must be suspended until safety concerns have been addressed.

38.3 Bulk

With bulk cargoes, while personnel safety concerns are still paramount, the primary issue is damage to the vessel that can occur while loading and discharging and the correct monitoring of the ballasting programme while loading:

- The cargo temperatures and chemical content must be as declared
- the holds should be properly prepared with burlapping of the bilges if required
- all the temperature gauges and stress monitors and water level alarms, if fitted, must be in order
- the ballast programme and hold sequence must be rigidly adhered to during the loading
- all personnel must use the outboard side of the deck and keep away from under the loaders and discharge grabs
- when operating the hatches, all personnel must be clear and a watch kept for any hydraulic leaks.

38.4 General Cargo

With general cargo, there are problems to personnel, the ship and the cargo:

- If using ship's gear, keep a careful watch on the crane or derrick wires for any sign of wear or breakage
- ensure that the stowage plan is kept to, with good separation between the consignments
- check any essential changes to the plan are marked and the stability is adjusted for the changes
- ensure that the cargo is dunnaged and lashed securely
- keep the proximity between the various cargoes compatible with their composition
- ensure that cargoes affected by heat are not stowed against the engine room bulkhead

- insist that all personnel operate on the outboard side of the ship
- make sure that barges are secured properly alongside before loading
- ensure that all shore labour leaves the hatches after the shift
- prior to closing any hold, check that all lighting is switched off and the fuses pulled.

38.5 Deck Cargo

Deck cargo comes in all shapes and sizes, each type requiring its own specific lashing and stowage, and there are specialist publications about them. A few generalisations can be made:

- If loading any heavy items that can be classified as heavy lift, for stowage either in the hold or on deck, ensure that you have calculated the heel and stability of the vessel when the weight is taken if using your own ship's gear. When using ship's gear for the loading it is quite normal in some ports for the loading to be done by the ship's officers and crew. If using more than one winch, each person driving a winch must be able to see you clearly or have communication with you during this procedure
- ensure that the place on deck where the cargo is to be positioned has been properly prepared. If under lashings are required, these must be laid out beforehand and the appropriate dunnage laid to allow the lashings freedom of movement when the cargo is in place
- when containers carrying liquid are loaded, they must not be allowed to rub against each other. Also ensure that chemicals are well separated according to their specifications

- if deck cargo is already in a framework, such as boats, remember to ensure that the frame is secured to the deck not the cargo. In other words, do not take any lashing directly over the cargo. The reason for this is, should the working of the ship in seas cause the deck to flex and strain any lashing you might have added, damage to the cargo can result. Any cargo frame should be lashed to the deck. Don't forget that spot welding can be done to secure such framing in place.

Spot welding can be used to secure framing.

Once, when loading heavy military equipment in New York, the frames supplied with the cargo were very flimsy. The Chief Officer noted this and called a halt to the loading while they were investigated further. We then sat together and designed our own requirements for carrying this cargo, which resulted in another three days alongside. The company and the shippers were not happy with what we had done until the cargo arrived in perfect order and the stowage design became standard for future shipments. The moral of this story is that if you are not happy with the deck stowage arrangements, or any stowage arrangements for that matter, raise your objections and if necessary call the Master and explain what you consider the problem to be.

You must ensure cargo is safely stowed, no matter who the customer is.

Regardless of who is responsible for the lashing and securing, you have a responsibility for the safety of the ship and, if you feel that the stowage or lashing of the cargo could cause damage or endanger the ship, this is the time to say so. If the Master wishes to proceed with the cargo as it is, then at least a note of protest about your objections should be issued.

39 Cargo Holds

On any ship type, your cargo is the reason for the ship's existence. The proper planning, loading, stowage, carriage and discharge should be the focus of all staff, after navigation and the safety of the ship and those onboard. Paramount in this is where the cargo is stowed, in tanks, holds or on deck.

Incorrectly stowed cargo may not end up where it was intended.

Each year cargo is destroyed, damaged or contaminated by seawater entering the holds of ships, both old and new. The majority of these occurrences are on older ships, but maintenance of hatch covers is a general problem on ships today.

The older a ship gets, the more problems it may have, particularly if it has been badly maintained. When joining a ship a quick look for any rust staining inside the hold at the tops of the coamings will tell you the story, as will the state of the rubbers, drain channels and compression bars. Signs of hatch sealing tape or foam sealant can also be a sign of potential leaking, although this is not necessarily a sign of poor hatch seals. Your hatches are weathertight not watertight. Submerge any hatch in water long enough and it will leak. Hopefully this will not happen during your time onboard but there are times during bad weather when the ship takes heavy seas on the decks, particularly on the forward hatches. If you are on an old ship, taking a grain cargo across the ocean in northern winter, would it not be prudent to take every care that you can of the cargo? I think so and if I had the hatch tape and foam available, I would consider it a responsible decision to use it, not as a repair but as an additional measure of care of the cargo.

39.1 The Testing of Hatch Covers

It would be easy to say that these should be tested before loading a cargo, but for ships on short haul voyages it is usually unnecessary. Before waiting for the annual loadline survey they should be tested periodically, on older ships more frequently than new ships. Certainly if I was setting off on a grain voyage across the Atlantic on an old ship I would test my hatch tops very thoroughly indeed, not wishing to be faced with a green topping to the cargo at the other end.

Most of us tend to use the hose test and there is nothing wrong with this provided it is done properly. Consider the force of water hitting your hatch tops in a storm and then use your hose to try to emulate it. You should ensure that your hatchtops are well battened down with the drain holes free and the non-return valves unblocked.

When you use the hose make sure that it is directed at the seals around the hatch sides and along each seal on the top, with the nozzle close to the seal. Try hard to get the water in!

Non-return valves are sometimes more of a hindrance. With many of them being made of plastic they often get washed away in heavy weather or broken by various means.

It is wise to keep a few spares in your stores but should you find that you are short you can attach a length of hose to the drain, put a ‘u’ bend in it and secure the hose end up under the hatch coaming. Make sure the open end is below this though!

Another way of checking is by using a chalk test. This has to be done in very good weather at sea as it involves opening the hatch tops. If done in port it could mean a delay in cargo operations. It is a test that takes longer than the hose test but it will give you a very good indication of the state of the rubber seals on the compression bar. All you have to do is open your hold and rub white chalk along the compression bar. Then close the hatch and batten down tightly. When you open the hatch again you look for the chalk marking on your rubber seal. If it is a continuous unbroken line your seal is good, the wider the chalk line the better your seal. If you do not see this mark the area will need repair.

39.2 Hatch Repair

Rubber seals harden over the years and, as they harden, they become less effective. When you examine the rubbers and see heavy grooving it suggests that the bearing pads that your hatch rests on have become worn down, so the whole weight of the hatch is now resting on the rubber seals. These pads will need to be built back up to specification.

When repairing your seals you should not try to insert small pieces of rubber. Rather, insert a longer length up to around 2 metres. Remember to clean out the channel first and coat with a good anti-corrosive paint. Clean the ends of the old rubber that the new rubber will butt onto to ensure that the adhesive will coat each end properly. Skilled seafarers can scarf the rubbers to ensure a more secure joint. However, it is recommended by manufacturers that when the rubber seal is in need of repair the whole rubber length should be replaced, rather than just that section. In all my time at sea we have always repaired sections as not only have we never had enough rubber to replace the whole section, but time would often have precluded this. Whether shipowners are prepared to accept the expense of this or allow skilled shore labour to be called in for this replacement, when only a small section of the rubber has been damaged, is also doubtful.

When checking your cleats, ensure that the rubber washers are in place. During any voyage the ship is working and will be flexing the decks and hatches, so periodically the crew have to tighten the cleats and this should be part of your weekly work list. The rubber washers allow for the flexing and assist in keeping the cleats tight. Cleats can disappear over the side during bad weather so make sure that you have spares. Cleats should not be bar tight as this will force the hatch rubbers down onto the compression bar too hard and cause damage to the rubbers.

39.3 Monthly Check of Hatches

- Cover tops, undersides and side panels - check for corrosion or cracks
- sealing arrangements - check rubbers, compression bars, drainage channels and non-return valves
- hatch cleats and rubbers - check for missing, corroded or broken
- chains or wire pulleys
- guide rails and track wheels
- stoppers
- hydraulic system
- pontoon hinges and locking pins
- coamings, stiffeners and brackets - check for any sign of corrosion and cracking, particularly at the corners of the hold and the deck plating in the way of the coaming.

39.4 Ladders

Another strange custom of the sea is that if ladders are in holds or tanks then a certain amount of damage or corrosion is acceptable, yet if they are outside on deck where they can be seen then they must be repaired.

The most common damage that occurs in any hold on a dry cargo ship is to the ladders. It is rare for any such ship, particularly a bulk carrier, not to have some damage to its ladders within a voyage or two. All too often this goes unnoticed as the damage cannot be found until it is too late. The stevedores certainly will not report it either. On older vessels corrosion plays its part and many of us are familiar with the odd missing step or corroded rung. While a bent rail can be acceptable provided the safety of the ladder is not compromised, any damage which could result in an accident must be attended to. This sometimes is not as easy as it sounds. Damage that has been observed as being caused by shore labour in a port is their responsibility to fix but other damage must be the ship's responsibility. All too often damage to a ladder cannot be safely reached by ship's staff and this requires the use of scaffolding or a cherry-picker. This means shore equipment and labour and a delay in work while the repair is effected, none of which will make you popular with any operator. Quite a few will delay repairing the ladders until the next dry dock if they can.

If it is possible, for the safety of all and to protect the ship, the ladders should be inspected prior to arrival. If it is not, then they should be inspected as soon as possible on opening up the holds and before anyone uses them. Most ships have ladders fore and aft in the holds and if a ladder is deemed to be unsafe then it must be clearly marked and closed off until repaired. In a number of ports you can be helped in this as, owing to the general state of ships' hold ladders, they have a safety inspection before work commences and they will order any unsafe ladders to be closed off or repaired if required.

While on this subject don't forget to do the same for your tank ladders as well. Just because it is crew using them rather than shore labour does not make the safety requirement any less stringent.

39.5 Lighting

Lighting in holds is a nuisance as, not only do you have to try to maintain it, but there is the danger of damage to the cabling and an ever present possible fire risk. Even replacing light bulbs can be hazardous and in many ships where lighting is built in, after some years the fuses are pulled and portable cargo lighting is rigged from above. The main requirement is that adequate lighting is provided for crew to work safely and, to prepare for this, have the cargo lights, whether fixed or portable, checked before they are required. If fixed lighting is present, even if it is working correctly, the fuses should always be pulled when the hatches are closed as a precaution against any electrical damage.

You might find it wise, during your meeting with the supervisor before work in the hold commences, to state what checks have been made and request that, if there is any complaint or problem, the duty officer is notified so that he can arrange additional lighting.

39.6 Completion of Loading or Discharge

Before you close the hatch you must ensure that all debris is clear of the channels and that the drains and non-return valves are clear. Cargo is damaged on ship after ship because of these very simple checks are being overlooked in the hurry to close the hatches and sail. It is better to spend an extra hour or two ensuring that any water that does leak in through the hatch rubbers can run freely down the channels and out of the drains.

As a final thought, don't think that the P&I Clubs are there just to throw money out if the cargo is damaged. Should they find hard evidence that your hatch tops have been poorly maintained and that the leaks that damaged the cargo have been ongoing, they could place a warranty on the damaged cargo. In other words, refuse to pay out on the grounds of your negligence.

40 Insurance

A considerable part of your job onboard is accident avoidance. When damage or accidents occur you will spend a lot of time dealing with them. All accidents, unless very small, will involve claims and insurance of some type, just as in your home. Differing policies apply but, in the end, someone has to pay. Your part in this affair, as an employee of the company, is to try to ensure that accidents do not happen and, if they do, reduce the extent of the accident and ensure that your company's case is supported properly by documentary evidence that Is clear and concise.

At sea you have, within your SMS, a systematic process for accident prevention with laid down procedures for drills, work and general safety practices that are part of the daily life. However, in port there are far more variables.

In the event of an incident or allegation which gives, or may give, rise to a third party claim, there are certain actions you should always take and certain actions you should never take.

Always:

- Call your owner or operator
- investigate every allegation of injury or damage
- collect evidence or documentation relating to the incident, including any defective equipment. Store it in a safe place and label the pieces of evidence. Throw nothing away
- take photographs of any damage or circumstances relating to the incident
- instruct witnesses to write a review of what they saw and heard and to draw a diagram if possible. This should be carried out as soon as possible after the incident. Write personal notes about the incident yourself
- ensure all accident reporting procedures and requirements are adhered to, eg MAIB reporting.

Never:

- Allow a surveyor or lawyer onboard the ship or to interview crew members until he has identified himself and produced appropriate authorisation to satisfy you that he is acting for your owner or your P&I Club
- allow surveyors or lawyers acting for the opposing parties onboard, unless you have authorisation to do so
- provide written material or physical evidence to opposing lawyers and surveyors. If in doubt, do not give anything to anyone or let anyone examine anything
- give a personal opinion about who or what was responsible. Keep to the facts. Again, if in doubt, say nothing
- allow crew members to express opinions

- admit liability either verbally or in writing
- sign a document that you know contains incorrect information. This includes making false entries in logbooks
- think that the problem will go away if you do nothing.

You might think that some of the above does not concern you as the Captain will be dealing with the problem. It is not unknown for certain lawyers, surveyors and assessors, working for those who may wish to claim against your ship and company, to wait until the Captain is off the ship before trying to board and inspect the ship or talk to crew members. Incidents might take place when the Captain is ashore. These matters do directly concern you and you will be wise to read the above carefully and have your officers read it as well, so that there is absolutely no uncertainty as to what their actions should be, who they should speak to and who they allow onboard.

40.1 P&I Clubs

Each P&I Club is a 'not for profit' organisation. It is a mutual association of shipping companies coming together paying their premiums and sharing in the costs. Like an insurance policy there are clauses, and the amount your company pays determines the extra insurances you obtain. On the surface this would seem to make no difference to you. However, the more paid out for accidents on your ship, the higher next year's premiums will be. If the owners have to pay rapidly escalating premiums, they are less likely to be listening to requests for pay rises or welfare amenities.

Your job, as the Chief Officer, is to assist in caring for the company's interests. Just because the company has a P&I Club does not mean that the costs are all necessarily paid. The company will have agreed deductibles to be reached before any P&I payout is made and, as already stated, there are certain clauses that may govern the proportion of any insurance claim.

The best way we can assist any club is to reduce the number of claims and this is achieved by your active leadership in safety and professional practice onboard.

Always remember that, in dealing with the P&I Club representative, he is not there to blame you or try to get you into trouble with the company. He is there to find out what went wrong, identify what can be done to alleviate the situation, and ensure that it does not happen again. He is on your side, so tell him the truth, regardless of who has done wrong.

When a ship enters port it is seen by some as a sweetshop, with lots of goodies to obtain. False claims are made and, in some ports where the ship is seen as a floating pension plan for the stevedores, slipping on an oily deck is a popular claim.

40.2 Accidents and Accident Prevention

At sea there is a routine system of safety guided by the SMS, the safety meetings and the general safety routine of the ship. However, in port there are far more variables, such as the shore labour on the ship. The shore labour are bound by any ship's regulations provided that they have been advised of them.

You can send ahead to the port your safety requirements for working on the ship, what PPE is required, where shore personnel may go and where they may not and that any accident is to be immediately notified to the OOW. Any safety issue is also to be reported to him. You can finish with an invitation to their safety officer to come onboard to discuss these issues. Don't hold your breath on that one though. In all the years of giving such invitations, I never saw one.

By sending such a safety requirement ahead to the port you are beginning to cover your ship and company. When you arrive they will have their own regulations for you to sign, but always remember to sign anything from the port as 'sighted only'.

Before port entry make a point of inspecting your decks. Not a general inspection, but one purely with safety in mind. What you are looking for is:

- Oil leaks, particularly from the hydraulic lines and cranes
- loose wires and ropes than can be tripped over
- if you have cranes, that they are clean and their screens are washed

- that all the deck lighting is working and, if you have portable lights for hold or overside working, that their electrics are safe and that the safety covers are properly fastened
- if you have hatches, that the hatch and any deck openings can all be clipped back properly and will not swing shut accidentally.

In fact anything that can affect the safety of those working there and which can be remedied by your crew before arrival.

If an accident occurs on deck it is essential that the casualty is dealt with immediately. In most ports they will have their own first aid station and will have arrangements for calling medical assistance to the scene if required. Some ports will not have these arrangements, in which case you will have to do what you can. It is wise to ensure that you have a first aid kit to hand in the deck office that the OOW can use immediately although, when possible, it is far preferable that the shore side medical team tend their own.

For more serious accidents shore assistance will be required. While the casualty is being attended to, either on deck or in the ship's dispensary, do try to get the accident report started as soon as possible. If your standing orders are followed, photographs of the area will have been taken, weather, lighting and deck condition will all have been noted and witnesses' statements will be in preparation. If the situation precludes getting these statements then at least get the names.

Inform the Master as soon as possible of the situation as he will soon be in the thick of it.

If an accident occurs in the port to any of the ship's crew, once again the same procedure should be followed, remembering that this time it is the ship that will be making the complaint. Too many times in the past ports have been able to ignore crew injuries on their property. To assist with this you should make out an accident report even though it did not take place on the ship.

41 Dry Docking

Prior to arrival in dry dock, you will be told the draughts and trim required for the dock and whether you will have time at the lay-by berth to arrange this prior to entry or if you must have it on arrival. If you are going in immediately on arrival you may also need to have tanks open and ventilated ready for entry.

You should also have a copy of the work list scheduled for the ship. Remember that it could be another five years before your ship gets the chance to get many of the problems sorted out. Ensure that the deck officers and Bosun also have the list of deck repairs that are taking place during the stay.

There are certain standard items that you should always include on a deck department dry dock repair list:

- Shore gangways to be provided
- shore fresh water

- sewage lines to be connected unless you really are in a place where there is a shore toilet
- protective coverings for the accommodation alleyways, public rooms and cabins such as yours, the Captain's and Chief Engineer's which will be used by shore visitors
- garbage skip placed on the deck for regular removal and replacement
- the anchor cables to be ranged, broken and the first shackle replaced with the last
- anchor lockers to be cleaned out and painted
- gangways to be lifted off their platforms for examination and repair
- boats to be lifted ashore. This gives you the opportunity for a complete overhaul of the davits and to replace or end-for-end the falls. It also provides the opportunity to paint the boats. Many fibreglass boats become dulled by the sun and should be repainted in fibreglass orange paint. This is a good opportunity to get the perspex glass changed in the coxswain's position if you have enclosed boats
- portable lavatories for the shore labour. This stops them entering the accommodation
- mud removal from the DB tanks
- galley uptakes to be steam cleaned
- shore fumigation of galley and storerooms if infestation is present
- crew transportation (if this is required in the yard).

Hopefully, the Captain will deal and discuss the ship management issues with you during the dry dock, but the areas of deck repairs and the work, safety and security are still directly under your jurisdiction, as is the management of your department. If on studying the work list you are seriously concerned about the removal of important repairs that you consider necessary, this is the time to discuss them with the Captain. If he also considers them important, together you have far more chance of getting them done.

41.1 Dry Dock Safety Meeting

You should ensure that the safety officer, or you if you are so designated, calls a safety meeting before arrival to discuss the various safety problems that will arise in the dry dock.

Your two immediate concerns are fire risks and security. You will find that the dockyard will have its own measures in place for these concerns but your internal ship precautions are still your responsibility. By calling such a meeting, you can at least alert the crew to all the additional dangers while the ship is in the dock. There could well be crew who have never been in a dockyard situation before.

While most of the ship's personnel will be on daywork, there will need to be a watch system established and I strongly recommend that you ensure that you have an officer on the day rotation responsible for dealing with all visitors to the ship. In addition, you will require a night watchman to ensure the security of the ship and to visit the hot work areas. You should make up your watch lists prior to arrival and post them.

The need for strict wearing of PPE should be discussed, particularly safety helmets.

Ensure that you have a well equipped first aid kit ready for use in the ship's office.

41.2 In the Dry Dock

The better you have prepared your department for the docking, the better your management in the dock will be and the easier time you will have.

On arrival, ensure that the dockyard puts the protective covering for the accommodation decks in place. If not then you will have to order this and have the crew put it down. The 'no smoking' notices must be in place and the regulations for PPE strictly enforced.

You know that each day you will be inundated with shore staff attending the morning meetings so make sure that you have prepared for this. Certain plans are bound to be required, such as the general arrangements and hull, so get them out ready. Places will be required for changing and messing arrangements will have to be dealt with. Some of this or all of this could be your responsibility.

If messing is in your province, it is essential that the Cook is informed about how many he will be cooking for each day and that a strict record is kept of the extra meals that are served.

You will be told what work your crew can and cannot do in the dock and this will differ from country to country and union to union. Hopefully, your crew will be able to coat areas of bare metal where work has been done. Keep an ongoing checklist of the work that is going on and the work that has been completed. When work is done, rather than leave it for the superintendents, ensure that you are satisfied with the workmanship.

Communication is essential and you must ensure that there is a system in place for your portable personal communications to be recharged each evening ready for the next day. Good management often depends on the small things.

Keep the Master advised each morning about what is going on. In the dry dock he should be largely superfluous, at least on a well run ship. There are times however when his support, presence and advice may be required, particularly with any problems with the dockyard personnel or if you have a dispute with the superintendents.

You really are not in the business of having disputes with the superintendents, no matter how provoked you may feel. If there is a matter on which you feel strongly then see the Captain and let him deal with them. If you are in a rare company that still has a deck superintendent you will have a sympathetic ear regarding your deck repairs and you will be able to learn from him during the docking.

41.3 Dry Dock safety and Security

The security officer and the ship's safety officer should arrange a meeting with their dockyard counterparts to discuss the dockyard plans for these responsibilities. If the dockyard is a secure area you should not be required to provide crew for manning the accesses onto the ship.

The days when all the plugs from the hull was your responsibility and were dumped in your cabin or office with labels on are long gone, but you still should, prior to departure, check that all the plugs have been replaced. Embarrassing to leave the dock and then have to come back for one small plug.

For the various inspections of tanks it is essential that the surveyor or superintendent is accompanied by a crew member, preferably an officer or cadet, and that communications are maintained with the inspecting party. Open spaces on the decks must be cordoned off and warning notices put in place.

The only way to keep track of hot work is to maintain in the ship's office a list of work, with times and dates, and to establish a regular security check. This should be carried out even if the dockyard has its own system in place for the simple reason that, regardless of the dockyard, the ship is still the responsibility of the ship's staff and this cannot be delegated to any other party.

Theft is a major problem in any port, but even more so in a dockyard. Immediately on arrival stow your lifebuoys away off the decks and remove your lifeboat stores into a locked area unless you have enclosed boats that can be locked. If you have rescue boats remove the outboards and stow them away.

The fire equipment is more problematic. In the event of a fire you will need access to this quickly so it cannot be stowed away. However, nozzles, especially if brass, should be brought into the ship's office where they can be easily accessed if required.

All lockers should be kept locked when not in use. Cabins, which are the natural targets for the casual thief, should always be locked and anyone found in the accommodation area must be challenged. Remove and lock away any portable equipment on the bridge, such as binoculars, recorders and cameras and ensure that the bridge is kept locked at all times when not in use.

41.4 Anchors

Anchors should be ranged in dock.

As standard practice both anchors and cables should be walked back out of the chain lockers and ranged along the dock bottom. All the shackles should be opened up and inspected, replacing where necessary.

The outboard length on each cable should be changed with the inboard length.

The chain locker should be inspected, the bitter end connection checked, the chain locker cleaned and coated and drains cleaned out.

Before the cables are taken back they should all be marked.

Ask whether the crew can paint the anchors. This can be done in the dock and then, as each is heaved up to an upright position, they can be completed.

41.5 Completion

It is important that the ship refloats with the tanks in the same condition as when you arrived. This means that the soundings should be the same and tanks filled or trimmed to reflect that. Check that all the plugs have been replaced and that any holes cut in the bottom have been welded tight.

If any ship's gear is missing, put this as a note of protest to the shipyard and claim for it. Minor items will often be replaced without a problem. You might find that you have to fight for some things as the attending superintendents will not be too interested, only seeing the 'big' picture, and will consider a missing wrench unimportant while it may be the only one you have!

At the end of the dry dock you will be expected to sign for the work done for your department. Do not sign for any work that has not been completed or that you are not satisfied with. If poor work has been done you should have raised the matter with the attending superintendents in time for it to be completed properly.

You will learn that in dry dock there are many issues at play. The superintendent is worrying about his reputation for saving the company money and keeping within or below the budget. The yard is concerned with the quotes and time penalties. The surveyor is trying to ensure that his neck is not on the line for approving certain conditions, seeing that the ship is kept in Class, but also not upsetting the owners of the ship, particularly if they are a large company. Then there is the crew who are, quite reasonably, only interested in scuttling down the gangway at the end of the working day. That leaves you, the Captain and the Chief Engineer to try to ensure that the repairs that you consider important are carried out in the way you wish.

Letter to a New Chief Officer

You will have noticed throughout this book constant references to relationships with people, dealing with them, caring for them and all the other facets of group interaction. A major part of the art of leadership is communication and ensuring that people understand why you require certain things to be done. This not only shows courtesy to those who you need to obey you, but hopefully provides you with a willing and cooperative workforce rather than a resentful one.

The companies you work for will all have their own ideas of what they require from you, but the responsibility you accept does not depend on them, it depends on you. The more you show you are able to accept, the more you will have. With your increasing acceptance of responsibility comes your growing authority.

You might say that much of what I have said is 'your responsibility' is the Captain's duty. In some instances this is true but, if the Captain does not do this or is not interested, does that mean that no one does it? The Captain looks to you for support, as you look to him. Part of this support is to constantly think of what needs to be done. If both of you are thinking this way, then there is far more chance of problem circumstances being noticed and dealt with, before they grow into more serious situations.

There is no guarantee that the Captain of the ship to which you are appointed is going to be the man you want, or even like, or that the officers you have under you are of a standard that you deem to be suitable. I would like to say that this doesn't matter, but of course it does and it will affect the way in which you do your job. You must overcome these problems if you are to continue at sea. No voyage lasts for ever, there will be other Captains and other ships, but if you can carry on and do your job to the best of your ability, you have nothing to reproach yourself for. However, do remember that it is not the Captain's job to get on with you, it is your job to get on with him. Your profession, your rank and the tradition of the sea requires you to support the Captain in his authority as Master of the ship.

Do read and continue learning about your profession. Many subjects have only a brief reference in this book and they deserve far deeper study for the professional officer. You will find that many of the subjects studied for your Master's certificate have not been fully discussed during your time in college.

In present times, with all the aids, communications advice and courses, a considerable number of ships are getting into trouble for one main reason: poor seamanship which can only be learnt by hard practical lessons. The neglect of this subject is now becoming more and more apparent as the accidents continue. If you are serious about remaining at sea, ignore those who say seamanship is not so important, it's just as important today as a century ago, in fact more so as the design of ships has become less concerned with the seakeeping aspect, and more concerned with the financial. Seamanship is not just about learning the crafts of the sea, which are constantly evolving in keeping with new ships and new equipment, but it is the appreciation of the environment in which you and your ship inhabit. The ability to read the ship and the sea provides the real skill of seamanship that can only come from a foundation of experience and good basic training in the same.

Many would laugh if you said that you learn from being up to your waist in seas on your decks, hooked and holding onto a safety line while trying to work with the other hand, but you certainly gain an appreciation of why safety lines should be rigged, checking them to make sure they are properly secured and sound, and why the saying of 'one hand for the ship, and the other for yourself' is a most sensible statement!

If you intend to remain at sea and become a Captain, the more you learn now about his work and responsibilities, the better prepared you will be for that day. Ask if you may, under the Captain's supervision to anchor the ship, make port approaches and departures and deal with the port officials. It is very strange that this kind of training is rarely carried out on ships, yet in the aviation industry it is common.

Above all else, understand that, as Chief Officer, your responsibility, apart from the engine room, encompasses the entire ship. You have to learn that what you passed by in your previous ranks, you must now stop and examine.

What you do and what you say will be watched and repeated by the crew, and whereas your deficiencies were tolerated by the ship when you were a junior officer, you will now be under far more critical appraisal.

In the past, many went to sea for the way of life, and the good times far outnumbered the bad experiences. Most of us enjoyed our life at sea and it was accepted that all onboard should have fun doing their job. Sadly, on too many ships, the fun element seems to have gone leaving behind just work, sleep and waiting to go home. Ships should not be like this. There is no IMO or company rule saying you cannot have fun, so, when you can, try to see if this can be part of the shipboard life. Your influence as the Chief Officer can assist considerably toward this, whether it is organising barbecues, crossing the line days or sports occasions, in fact anything that can bring those onboard together for enjoyment that can break the monotony.

Enjoying life at sea should not be consigned to the past.

In closing, I will leave you with my favourite summary of the character of the seafarer. If those from other countries substitute their nation's name, the words are just as appropriate and deserving as the sea has never had borders of any race or nationality.

> *'The Sea has formed the British character, and the essential Britain is to be found in those who follow it. From blue waters they have learnt mercifulness and a certain spacious tolerance for what does not affect their craft, and they have also learnt in the grimmest schools, precision and resolution. The sea endures no makeshifts. If a thing is not exactly right, it will be vastly wrong. Discipline, courage.....and a contempt for all that is pretentious and insincere are the teaching of the ocean and the elements, and they have been the qualities of all ages of the British sailor.'*
>
> *John Buchan, 1875-1940*

Acknowledgments

Web Rigging Supply Inc, 27W966 Commercial Avenue, Lake Barrington, IL 60010, for their permission and assistance with ropes and wires.

Jotun Paints (Europe) Ltd, for their assistance with paints.

Safinah Ltd, marine coatings and paint consultants, for their assistance with paints.

IMO Guidelines for Ships Operating in Arctic Ice-Covered Waters

ILO Convention 180 – Seafarers' Hours of Work and the Manning of Ships

IMO Resolution A.890(21) – Principles of Safe Manning

MSC/Circ.10.14 – Guidance on Fatigue Mitigation and Management

TNO Report (Houtman et al 2005) – Fatigue in the Shipping Industry

MSN 1767 (M) – Hours of Work, Safe Manning and Watchkeeping

IMO Resolution A.868(20) – Guidelines for the Control and Management of Ships' Ballast Water to Minimize the Transfer of Harmful Aquatic Organisms and Pathogens